Lars M
The

Translated from the Norwegian
by Becky L. Crook

Broken Dimanche Press

The Black Signs
Lars Mørch Finborud

A Broken Dimanche Press Publication
Berlin 2014

The book appeared originally as *De svarte skiltene* © Copyright Gyldendal Forlag AS 2013
Translated from the Norwegian by Becky L. Crook
Translation supported by NORLA
Design by FUK Graphic Design Studio
Editor: John Holten

First edition: 1000

ISBN: 978-3-943196-29-0

I

They say old houses are comprised of their good memories, not cracks or stains, but in this case I doubted it was true. To call it a house would be off the mark; an abandoned temple or unapproachable fortress was more fitting. A picket fence: the scaling-wall, and a dried up well: the moat. The structure was pocketed in invisible weather, which was void of wind, chill, moisture, warmth, pressure, as though the atmosphere had merely slipped away without a trace, leaving us standing there. Still, in my dark blue suit and with a leather satchel full of legal documents, I felt strangely at ease. Reassured by the quiet summer day, it was hard to imagine anyone within the fortress preparing boiling oil in a large black cauldron or collecting boulders to cast down on intruders. At its core, the building reminded me of my deceased aunt's house, where the family used to gather for celebrations, though this one, it should be noted, was in significantly inferior condition. I approached the gravel lane. With each step, I became aware of a low rumbling sound emanating from the building. My first thought was that the sound originated from a nearby construction site, since it lessened now and then, but the hum reverberated throughout my body. Suddenly, the tone rose abruptly, engulfing me and becoming increasingly more insistent. I covered my ears with my hands, bent my head towards my chest and knelt down, blindly. The thunderous undertone swept back and forth until it was overpowered by a piercing sound. From the wall of noise there now rose a clear, quivering tone that knocked me breathless. It was a battle between opposing voices—provocative, complaining, mischievous, inquisitive, embracing, enraptured, enraged—together forming an all-encompassing tone to devour anything animate and drain it of will. A sorrowful song, sung with much too much empathy. A dirge? Had I been a foot soldier in an army ordered to storm this palace, I would have tip-toed to the back row to tie my shoelaces while the cavalry invaded. But here I was, a lawyer, whose job it was to inventory an estate, so my situation was actually much worse. I was the forsaken standard-bearer, riding solo across the plain toward the enemy's countless soldiers, flag in one hand, trumpet in the other. By the time I removed my hands from my ears, the rumbling had ceased. Or, perhaps it was still there, but my body must have adapted to it. At the end of the gravel lane, a black gate led me to a dazzling entrance. The enormous mahogany doors looked as if they had only yesterday been lacquered. A pair of soggy grey jogging shoes were the only sign that no one had been around for quite awhile. I continued on, courageously. The large key on the ring fit the lock, but though I turned both one way and the other, the door refused to budge. After checking that there were no security locks or hooks, I leaned my weight against the door and nudged. There was a small click, like a fingernail tapping against a tooth, but the door refused to give way. Placing my coat jacket as a go-between, I pounded against the door, blow after blow. Some strokes later, it was clear that, at this rate, either the door or my shoulder would sustain injuries. I would have to find another way in. I made my way around to the kitchen door. The key fit just as easily, but the door was even more resistant than the first. It was as though it had been welded shut from the inside, as if the house had been barricaded with an armoured shell. With both shoulders smarting, I decided to attempt the kitchen window next to the landing. If this didn't deliver the intended results, I would call up the office and ask them to organise a locksmith or send one of the firm's juniors over with a crowbar. I tapped gently on the two lowest panes of glass, leaned over the railing and felt my way up to the hinges. As the last hinge was released from its hook, the window fell outward with a blast. A cold, pent up pressure from within surged forward, flinging me violently backwards with the release, though I managed to grab hold of the banister at the last moment. Gazing up from the bottom stair, I saw for the first time that what I had mistook for the kitchen's pitch darkness, was in fact a wall of black metal plates, impenetrable, closely packed, placed like a wall in front of the window. The thought arose that someone might be standing in ambush behind this barrier, that maybe I wasn't coming to inventory an estate, but was breaking in to where my company was not desired, and where someone stood prepared to attack whoever tried to force entry. And I, the standard-bearer, had been nominated for this assault.

I reviewed the case information in my head. It had been over six months since anyone had seen the owner, who had inherited the estate from his grandmother two years earlier—the grandmother being, apparently, a highly respected cultural figure. The only person in the neighbourhood who had actually met the grandchild face-to-face was a Philippine housemaid working in the Austrian ambassador's residence. She spoke of heavy construction on the site some years ago and described several sightings of a figure, who must have been the grandchild. This man ran around in working clothes all hours of the day, giving directions to the continuous string of trucks that delivered supplies. She noted that he was attentive and kind, almost to a fault, and well, there was one more thing: "He always had something white in his beard." Otherwise, there was little else to go on. No school friends, relatives or colleagues. Even the grandmother, who by all appearances was something of a celebrity in her time, failed to show up in a public registry or in an online search. That pallets from West Africa were unloaded at midnight, didn't seem to bother the neighbours. It took a shabby garden to really get their goose. Or rather, it wasn't actually the vast garden that was a nuisance—because that was well hidden, tucked between the bows and curves of the majestic maples—but the neighbours lamented the flaking of the picket fence. And the large quantities of packaging that were blown onto their properties in heavy winds. Everyone has their limits, and when autumn arrived, the garden was revealed to be an enormous, abandoned refuse heap. Property standards, combined with perpetual unpaid bills, earned the grandchild the status of "officially disappeared." Now, here I was, charged with putting the estate in order.

My firm didn't specialise in inheritances. It had been my old drinking mate, Rolv Dysthe, who pulled me into the case. Rolv was that type of nightmare man-about-town from the university days in the 60s who hadn't progressed since the good old days. The oldest son of one of Larvik's lumber families, he had been demoted at an early age as the family's black sheep—undeservedly, according to him—and was found unfit to take over his father's business. As compensation, he therefore accepted a refined apartment in Camilla Colletts gate in the capital city, together with an envelope delivered each month to his post box, bulging with effective damage control. This is what enabled Rolv, at the age of only 20, to be in possession of his own tables at both Bristol and Pigalle as well as a table decked in white linen at Theatercaféen, which became his fixed reading spot for many years. Between the open sandwiches of beef burger, caramelised onions and decanters, his law books lay scattered about. He held colloquiums with the waiters and regulars. Not only did he often cause us pangs of jealousy due to his little red Jaguar and expensive, directly-imported jazz albums from the USA, he was also a real nuisance for those of us who were forced to supplement our student incomes by doing evening transcriptions for professors or stacking cases of beer at Bislett. Rolv took every opportunity to call us "prostitutes" and "tenant farmers," but kept conveniently mum about how his own bread was buttered. Because he was prohibited from bringing the Theatercaféen waitstaff to assist on his final exams, he failed with flying colours, leading to a rare visit from his father who had finally found a good enough reason to send his son far away. Four years passed in which we didn't hear so much as a peep from Rolv. Then, one day, he appeared with a private Swiss education under his belt, and the white linen tablecloths were once again set out on his favourite tables. He took the title of lawyer and bought himself a placement at a firm that was run by all the other partners. In exchange for a capital contribution, he received a respectable writing desk, postal address and the freedom, for the rest of his life, to cultivate his specialty, which was to sit on the steering committees of charitable organisations and cultural foundations. The happy days of the student union and the Christiania rowing club were long past. Which is why I was more than mildly surprised when the telephone rang with Rolv's voice sounding on the other end. The usually fiery and agitated voice was heavy and terse. I thought he must be calling to inform me that an old comrade had died, or that cancer had settled in his liver, but he inquired whether we could meet for lunch at Theatercaféen. He wasn't at liberty to discuss anything else over the phone. When Rolv arrived ten minutes late the following day—what he liked to call "African time"—his gloominess had all but disappeared. In his usual manner, he recalled how we used to dance ourselves halfway to death to "Lill Lindfors album with the blue cover" and Lee Morgan's "The Sidewinder" with young girls from the country schools. Unlike me,

Rolv could remember every detail about each girl I had dated, the names of fellow students and where they had all landed on the social ladder. He recalled the summer that we wildly memorised Wildenvey poems, and couldn't resist reciting the one about little Ellen: "You, dear young maid, who lays and shall die, let me tell you a fable, — your last," while I sat opposite him, smiled silently and harboured my own thoughts. Rolv had also mastered the art of surfacing less-affirming memories. "What was it that happened, actually, with that novel you took all those years to write, or was it just an excuse not to join in at our parties? In any case, it was a damn good excuse! Always zigzagging between literature and philosophy before you finally started chewing the fat with the rest of us on Karl Johan." But he knew exactly what had happened. My brother had died that year in an unfathomable frostbite mishap that was the consequence of just such drunkenness and revelry, a sober fact that resulted in my father handing over management of his law practice to someone else. In a way, I was lucky. At a young age, I had come to realise two truths that I would accept absolutely throughout my life: that I possessed no exceptional artistic talents and could live pleasantly by not bothering the rest of the world with my words. The other realisation — which was far more important — is that wealth and security allow one to more fully enjoy immersion into art and its labyrinthine tributaries. This, too, is a comfort. After the small talk, I noticed that Rolv recovered the tone he had used in his phone call the previous day. He had a proposition for me, a task on behalf of a group of people that he referred to as "of the old school". Basically, the job was an estate inventory. I was to go to a certain house, enter and report back. "One thing I *am* at liberty to tell you, is that the woman who once owned the house had friends in high places, also internationally, and they have begun to fear the worst." Rolv finished by assuring me that money posed absolutely no hurdles for his clients. Of course, my first question was why didn't Rolv take the job himself, if it really was so simple. I watched as he extracted a lengthy pause, tracing the words on the inside of his mouth with his tongue before answering: "Those whom I represent wish to attract as little attention as possible to the case. They don't want to hire a firm full of well-known lawyers and large, eavesdropping ears, but rather one that understands the meaning of discretion. Someone discreet who doesn't rub his nose in unpleasant odours. And that is you." He smiled stiffly.

Now, it seemed to me that our lunch at Theater-caféen had taken place years ago, but in reality it had been less than a week. If there was one thing Rolv was good at, it was finding others do to his job for him. It's a useful skill to develop in life. I was aware that my wife and I'd been going to bed early the last few years. So I said yes.

I removed the grandmother's folder from my leather satchel. My attention was drawn to the line stating "Profession." Originally, the words "Art Collector" had been written on this line, but had been crossed out bluntly with large, black pen strokes that soaked through to several pages. With the same pen, the perpetrator had written instead "Gatherer of Art." At first, I had believed the metal wall inside the window to be an emphatic safeguard to the house, but now I started to think it unlikely that this was an unassailable, armoured wall; it seemed rather to be a pile of metal plates stacked in front of the window. A brief council with myself produced the suggestion that I should go to fetch a drill or metal cutter, but I first decided to attempt entry from the rooftop. I found a ladder in a storage room beneath the kitchen entryway, propped it against the wall and ascended. As my head came above the drainpipe, I stopped short. What should have been a straight-edged roof was bulged out and torn in places, here and there swollen with structural protrusions. Something had started breaking through. I continued upward, found my footing firmly on the roof and reconnoitred. I took in the view high above the tall maple crowns. The house was located at such a height that made it possible to see out over all of Oslo. At the other end of the house, with the cityscape at my back, my eye caught at something red protruding from the drainpipe. This turned out to be a small glider plane. With decaying plastic wings and covered with wet leaves and earth, it felt like a sea creature in my hand. Brushing the leaves aside, I took a few backward paces and threw it forcibly into the air, as though my strength might endow it with able wings. The glider shot out some meters before whizzing downward, not even having reached the neighbour's garden. "Pity those who find the black box and only hear the bang." Following the curve of the glider, my eyes lit on the heavy clouds drifting toward me. The atmosphere returned with full force, and the sunlight blended with the blue grey clouds to form a damp, yellowish light. The sky pitched overhead like a well-worn hospital mattress. Soon it would rain. Time to get started. I lay on my stomach near one of the rooftop mounds and attempted to peer inside. Beneath the roof, my hand felt the same invincible wall of metal and it was neither possible to see further inside nor to enter the house through this fissure. It was impenetrable. But I wasn't yet ready to admit defeat. With my hand, I managed to pry out one of the metal plates from the top of the stack. I lifted it out, rolled onto my back and held the plate above me, apprehending my find. It was a sign.

THE GREAT AUK (THE DAWN OF TIME – 1848)
Previously widely distributed bird species of the northern hemisphere made extinct by Norwegians in 1848. The hunter Lauritz Odin Brodtkorb shot the last remaining specimen outside of Vardø in the spring of 1848 in the belief that it was a razorbill he had in his sights.

I rolled back over, thrust my hand down into the endless darkness and tore out another plate.

JAN HOLMBOE (1725 – 1767)
It was here that Jan Holmboe was run over by a horse-drawn carriage with a tipsy coachman on January 7, 1767. He died four days later at the hospital in Christiania from injuries suffered.

The purpose of the signs was unclear, but one thing was obvious: the signs had been brought into the house, so there must be an entrance somewhere. With newfound enthusiasm, I decided to try the veranda door in the garden. I climbed down the ladder and moved quickly around toward the back where I was met with an overgrown garden the size of a fifty meter swimming pool. Between the tangle of vines and fallen fruit lay pieces of plastic, wet cardboard and broken pallets. Large square shapes, void of grass, imprinted the yard, where something heavy had sat, pressing all life out of the earth. The place must have been swarming with activity not long ago. It looked as though someone had broken camp in the night, and moved on. A makeshift shower hung from a tree branch, a hose tied and held up by strong nails. Behind the tree were mounds of used toilet paper. The only semblance of a cultivated garden was a pavilion encapsulated in ivy, but even this was impossible to enter, the branches forming a tangled grid in front of the opening. I considered trying out a door to the cellar, which I had noticed on the east side of the building, but dismissed this alternative when I spotted a ramp that inclined up the veranda toward the first floor. Just as it should, the door opened without difficulty. A deluge of chilled air poured out toward me, spreading a flush of goosebumps up to my ears. Stepping aside to let the sunlight enter, I was able to make out the contours of a closet or small, oblong studio space. These few square meters had once comprised part of a much larger room, a library or dining hall, but most of the floor space was now occupied by stacks of metal plates. The chandelier had been ripped from the ceiling, cables hung by their joints from the stucco, and on the wall I could make out the remains of a recessed bookcase. What made the strongest impression on me, however, was that the villa was no longer held up by its own original structure, its backbone having been replaced by the metal totem poles. The old construction was destroyed and discarded, like a useless shell. I thought I should probably strike a match and get out of there, but as the building was a warehouse constructed of metal, I doubted it would do much good. Looking at the exalted pillars, I felt as though they might topple over, burying me alive out of sheer meanness. They towered above me, menacingly. What if the grandchild stood on the other side, waiting for the right moment to thrust them over on top of me? I pushed the thought away. It was unthinkable that the missing grandchild had been taking cover here, as it was a mere 10–12 degrees in the room. The only sign of life was a writing desk and a sleeping bag unrolled atop a mattress. Tools and extension cables lay on the floor in piles at the other end of the room. There was nowhere else to hide. Just above the tools hung a number of signs attached to three dimensional structures. They were assembled layer by layer on a small wall which stuck out into the room.

LENE UGELVIK (1914–1986)

In this place, Lene Ugelvik's red balloon was stolen by a gang of boys on March 23, 1918. She was inconsolable for the rest of the day.

THEODOR "THEO" DEVOLD (1986–)

This is where Theodor "Theo" Devold was denied an individual plan for psychiatric help, to which he had a right, from Sannes District Psychiatric Centre. He therefore remained on the same medications for a long time, which led to his developed addiction to a particular brand of pills.

GLITTERTIND

Norway's highest point, 2471 metres above sea level. Due to an undemocratic measurement standard, the point Galdhøpiggen, 2468 metres above sea level, received recognition of the title. But with its glacial cover, Glittertind is demonstrably Norway's highest point.

ANDREAS LIEBIG (1962–)

Sagene Church attempted to sack Liebig from his position as organist on the grounds that his interpretations of psalms and chorales was too emotional and progressive for the Protestant church's taste.

EVEN TORP (1880–1973)

The tram that should have arrived at Bislett at 6:20 p.m. was delayed by more than 12 minutes on March 7, 1934. As a result, Even Torp and his fiancé missed the first act of "Erasmus Montanus" at the National Theatre. An irritable mood settled over the household on this evening.

I read and read—and read some more. I couldn't tear my eyes away, and even memorised several of the signs. Running from one sign sculpture to another, I read frantically from all angles. It was then I realised what exactly lay before me. The pillars comprised thousands upon thousands of stacked black signs, each one containing the displaced residue of random human lives. The signs were identical to the city's blue signs, the ones that documented cultural-historical facts about where or how resistance fighters, nation builders and artists were born, lived or carried out their heroic deeds. These were precisely the same size, with rounded corners and a convex surface. Even the graphic design had been imitated down to the last detail. Just as the blue signs, the black ones were not limited to a particular historical context. They did not distinguish between events from the present or from the era when dinosaurs roamed the earth: every epoch was given equal representation. The only apparent difference was that the signs before me were black. The more I read, however, the more I understood that the black signs narrated a different manner of historical account. Whereas the blue signs painted a glowing picture of humanity's undeniable intellectual abilities, the black signs seemed derisive. They told about the history that we would most wish to forget and to separate ourselves from. That which was despised. Shameful. Illegal. Undervalued. Aggrieved. Unsightly. Petty. Untrue. Embarrassing. The black signs proposed an alternative history in opposition to the official version. They were a complaint. A protesting whine. A downright malicious and howling grudge. In and of themselves, the individual histories narrated on the signs were not particularly terrifying. The disturbing thing was the way in which the signs' latent criticisms were conveyed—with a frivolous, almost childlike tone. It was like a joke that you didn't understand, but in which you could sense that there was some very confident laughter involved. The signs grated on me in another way too: they reminded me of an extended comment field on the Internet or of a graffiti-covered bathroom stall, whose claims insist on being taken as seriously and with as much academic clout as any encyclopaedia. In my consternation, I only barely heard the clink of metal behind me.

My body stiffened so sharply that a swell of tension washed over my ears. Had the grandchild hidden himself after all, and come now to protect his life's work against an intruder such as me? Turning on my heel I let out a forceful scream, eyes shut. No response. Eyes open. There was no one. Just me and piles of what must have been millions of black signs. Relieved, I walked back out onto the veranda and filled my lungs with a breath of the humid summer air. A barrage of questions began to form in my mind. I had to find answers. Who could have conducted such thorough research to produce so many unique signs? What type of people have such vast resources at their disposal? Was it the grandmother or the grandson who was behind the outrageous undertaking, and were the signs the cause for my anxiety? I inhaled deeply and returned into the cold. Ransacked the desk. Tore up the carpet. Shook out the sleeping bag. And finally, I knocked on the walls to discover hidden rooms. Nothing. Nothing. No clue how to shed light on what this was all about. I sat on the bed to double check the documents. The grandson's file indicated several instances of petty criminal offences throughout his adolescence. At the age of 12, he had stolen a box of alphabet cereal, explaining in his defence that he intended to give it to his dyslexic friend. When caught stealing a donut worth fifty cents, he had behaved so provocatively to the shopkeeper that the latter lost his temper and beat the boy to a pulp. At the age of 16, he and a friend founded the YAE Association—Youth Against Everything, but were soon thereafter convicted of forgery and of tampering with the membership numbers. As the case unfolded, the police also discovered that the grandson was the chairman and head of over 70 associations. Strangely enough however, it appeared that his criminal record had been spotless for the past ten years. As I leafed through his impressive 8th grade transcripts, my eye caught on an object near the veranda door. What I had taken to be a step was actually a book. Whoever had placed it there must have believed that it would be immediately noticeable upon entering the room, but instead it had blended in with its surroundings. The book itself even resembled the black signs, bulging outward and challenging its own framework. I leaned over and gingerly picked it up, then sat down on the mattress to examine the find. The book was filled with hundreds of sheets of paper, glued page by page. It was a type of catalogue. A quick scan of the pages revealed that it contained a large number of handwritten letters to a person named Gustimoldo. Gusti-mol-do. Was he the character from *The Hunchback of Notre Dame* or an Italian knight? The name stuck in pronunciation like mildew on the tip of my tongue. I concluded that the letters must have been written by the grandson, as he referred in several places to "Grandma" and to her "collection." Every single letter began with the insistent salutation: Dear Gustimoldo. The grandson asks him to return home from his travels or self-imposed exile. Gustimoldo is accused of having abandoned their shared project, a project which the grandson complains of having been lured into. The bitterness increases proportionally with the grandson's realisation, slowly but surely, of his dependence on Gustimoldo to complete the work. "Come home, Gustimoldo. Come forth, Gustimoldo" is a phrase commonly repeated over and over again, and the grandson attempts to conjure up his friend, as if writing their shared history could bring him to life. Some of the letters were painful to read. Not because of the uncontrolled rage and longing that bubbled to the surface, but because Gustimoldo appears to have gone completely off track. An agitator. A demiurge. A *provacateur*. A philanthropist with an intense hatred of people. The grandson, on the other hand, had a more patient, condensed tone. But one that was also more resigned, more bitter and from what little I could gather, more dangerous. After reading the catalogue from cover to cover, I thought to myself: here we have two people who blame the entire human race for their own lack of humaneness. They were, to borrow a word from the grandson, "petit-nihilists" who enjoyed flirting with ideas of oppression, with totalitarian values and darkness stemming from pain, but who were only able to draw motivation and to find their platform within the confines of a safe democracy. The catalogue of the grandson's letters was periodically interrupted by several pages listing an index of something called "jutegnask", which had been sold at an auction. It seemed that only a portion of the index was included in the book, since the numbers jumped over several thousands of objects. The last item of jutegnask, unabashedly referred to as "Picasso's burst condom", is registered under the number "JG7912414". Whereas the jutegnask catalogue had been printed on a machine, the letters had been handwritten using a black marker. They must have been formulated in haste, as they contained several strikethroughs and arrows pointing to the margins. The handwriting often continued throughout several lines without ever having been lifted from the page. After a closer inspection, I realised that the correspondence was one-sided. There hadn't been a single response. Though the grandson refers to several postcards received from Gustimoldo, I was not able to find a single one among the catalogue. Another factor that puzzled me was that it did not seem as though the letters had been posted. There was no sign of an envelope or postage stamp, no visible fold marks or dates, no signature. I began to wonder whether the whole thing was a joke, and that I might be the victim of one of Rolv's latest antics. But no, it couldn't be a joke. The book's impact was much too overwhelming. It aroused in me a feeling of resistance that I hadn't felt in years. It offered a chance for correction, an alternative viewpoint and at the same time made me aware of exactly what I stood for, what it was that gets me up in the morning. One thing at least was clear: I could not put the book down. I studied the book intensely for several hours before finally getting up. As I walked out the door, I got that uncomfortable feeling one gets when you've forgotten to place one foot in front of the other. The building had numbed my senses. I had forgotten how cold it was inside, and although I knew that the low rumbling sound must still be present, I could no longer hear it. I curled into the sleeping bag and listened to the wind breezing through the maple trees outside. There was a whisper, but I couldn't determine whether it came from the leaves or the signs. What message were they trying to convey? It had begun raining and the first drops on the roof fell with a plunking sound. The rain reminded me of prolonged applause in concert halls. I could see through the veranda door that the sun was still shining far off. I thought of my father's American car, which hadn't been able to tolerate this kind of "meteorological cocktail." My father, who never entertained expensive habits or frittered away money that he didn't have, was captivated by this American beauty whose independent free spirit meant that the motor stopped working whenever the sun, rain or snow came out all at once. Mum used to tell me about the countless times he'd lugged the car on a rope to the nearest farm or gas station to get it under cover until the weather had normalized again. But Dad flatly refused to switch to another, more functional car. I remember how he used to take the American out of the garage every holiday and spend hours polishing it. After that, we'd take a ride up to Ekeberg Restaurant or Grefsenkollen for cake and soda.

They sat me on two pillows in the front seat and I can remember how the polished hood gleamed ahead of us. Not a scratch in sight, just meter after meter of blackness and the smell of polishing wax. The hood reminded me now of the black signs. They gleamed as well, and gave off a reflection. Maybe it was the bad air, the chill throughout my body, or merely the day's unexpected turn of events, but in any case, I fell asleep and was caught up in a strange nightmare. I, who hadn't dreamt a single thing for over 25 years, was suddenly swept away without a warning.

In the nightmare, Oslo was filled with black signs. Before the sign epidemic broke out, there were those who maintained that grass would one day grow over our cities again. Little did they know that the cities would one day be covered by black signs. Buildings and bus stops swelled to yet unnamed mountains as a mass of signs, numbering in the five digits, were affixed to their facades. The signs were always slipping, sliding down with a tremendous speed; the underlying city was their sounding board. On every street, pedestrians were faced with the morose gaze of black signs. People milled about restlessly, trying to find somewhere to hang their own black signs or to read others'. Lively discussions once again filled city squares and city streets. The night sky was lit by a strobe light, which had been erected in the hope of illuminating the signs in the best possible manner. After the commercial sign printers no longer accepted orders, people began setting up their own mobile printing presses and modified melting furnaces. Telephone cables, refrigerators, ATM machines, mufflers, streetcar rails, sewer pipes, lamp posts, light posts, steel girders, train sets, manhole covers. Everything was put into the furnaces. Everything except for the black signs. A tar-like smog hovered above the city, illuminated from below by flames from the same machines that belched it forth. Eardrums rumbled with the blast of distant sign-canons, which shot the black signs into the air in the hope that they would land atop buildings where there was more space than on the streets below. Signs landed on other signs, some didn't catch but slipped back down into what used to be the city's thoroughfares. Anyone hit by a sign blast did not die in vain. There was honour in a sign-induced death, and relatives had the opportunity to create a new black sign to allocate blame on the misfortune. As the wall space on buildings slowly but steadily filled up, people began affixing signs to horizontal surfaces. Roads, parks, sidewalks, and football fields were covered layer by layer with black signs that increased in height. The city as one might have remembered it in earlier times, disappeared little by little and old maps had to be destroyed. And even though Oslo was the birthplace of the black signs, the pandemic was so absolute that indigenous peoples in even in the most remote areas had begun creating signs. There were photos of trees in the rainforest jungles bowed over to a snapping point under the weight of so many black signs. A TV-programme from the Sahara showed a bleeding camel leaping around with a black sign fastened to its hump. Loved ones lost to cancer, authoritarian parents, crooked noses, bad punctuation, increasing housing prices, influenza, divorced parents, bad weather, bad acne, sexual assault, delayed job promotions, medicinal side-effects, dead pets, overcooked pasta, cold winter days, toothaches, infidelity and religious frustrations. The black histories were endless and there was no limit on the guilt that people assigned. Even those who led full, worthwhile lives somehow found a new meaning to their existence by dedicating themselves entirely to the production of signs. There was no stopping the spread of signs now. In the days before the outbreak, there had been some feeble measures to contain it. The police and the military were ordered to confiscate all black signs and the production of new signs was banned. The new laws were enforced with roadblocks, border shutdowns, curfews after sunset, raids of paramilitary sign-printing operations that were concealed deeply among groves of Norwegian spruce. There were rumours about drone attacks by foreign authorities who understood early on that a pandemic of this sort could turn into a global crisis if it wasn't stopped short. Governing PR agencies published photos and videos of signs that had been seized and melted down to deter and warn their citizens. Truth be told, however, these images infuriated the people, and the desired effects were minimal. The newly created sign tribunals held impromptu proceedings and pronounced thoughtless convictions. In the Prime Minister's speech, just days before declaring a full-on emergency, he declared to his people: "One must live with forgiveness, to have the ability to look beyond oneself to the bigger picture. One must move forward, with a gaze fixed to what's ahead. This is what it means to be human." Two days later, there were photos circulated of him and his family being driven around the city by their chauffeur and hanging up black signs wearing only their bathrobes. A few more days passed and it became clear that an official state authority no longer existed. Even the most respected police and foreign service officials now spent their days hanging up, exclaiming over, and discussing the black signs. The purpose and meaning of humankind, its only gratification, now consisted almost solely in being in contact with the signs.

For a long time now, the tale had been told that in the beginning, before the epidemic had spread irrevocably, a group of doctors, farmers, architects and engineers foresaw what would come to pass. Rather than building a boat or space rocket, they decided the only solution to escape the fate of the black signs would be to tunnel deep down into the earth's interior. One night, they woke their family and close friends and led them down into the tunnel. They thus avoided the infection. Below the earth's surface, they created a new society free of signs, free of guilt, and based on cooperation and trust. They lived off of stores of food and drinks that they'd stockpiled, in addition to roots and insects from the soil. After a time, they calculated that the earth must be covered completely in signs, and they ventured out of the tunnel and up to the surface. Just as predicted, swaths of green foliage had crept up over the crusted signage plates, streams ran and moist soil lay where one could begin cultivating hardy, shade-grown plants. Warmth from the Earth's interior circulated and smaller communities began to emerge. There is no one to confirm the legend or deny it. The truth is that no one cares anymore. I stand among the landscape of signs, observing myself in an idle snow plough, looking out across the devastation. Putting the vehicle into first gear, I plough straight through heaps of black signs. They bulge up like clay pigeons from every angle, barely missing the people I pass who gaze carelessly back at me. There has been a metal shortage for a long time now, and many people have simply lain down to give up. There is no food, they have given up caring, they just stand or lay motionless atop the black signs. Some bring up the good old days of the signs, while others weep over unrealized sign possibilities. One guy pulls himself up onto a heap and tries to incite a band of people to make their way north together. There are talk of mines up north, full of ores and minerals for making signs. "The light will shine once more from the North!" he rants as I steer the plough into a side alley. Out in front of the powerful headlight beams, I can see the contours of a group of people standing around gesturing at the signs, pointing out the best ones and nodding in agreement. Their energy has all but left them and they sway to and fro in order to find their balance, like birch trees in the wind. As I drive past, they sway in my direction. I realize that I am in possession of the sole surviving operational vehicle, and I am momentarily afraid that the crowd will try to hijack the snow plough, to use it to head north or to melt it down for metal, but instead they begin walking in a procession behind me. Do they believe I will lead them out of the curse of the signs, or are they nursing the hope that I will somehow take them to more black signs? Someone throws himself in front of the snow plough. In a quick manoeuvre, I manage to break just before I run over him. He stands and climbs up to the hood, begging me with urgency to hang up a black sign: "We want to see, do it for all of us." I hold my palms out flat to show that I do not have any black signs. He contorts and falls down onto the hills of signs. The journey continues, directionless. In my side mirror I can see a long trail of people following the plough like a dark veil drawn through the night. I switch to the highest gear, push the pedal to the floor and hear a thunderous rumbling. I cannot tell whether it is the snow plough hit by a falling sign, or the city that collapses, slowly but surely, at my back.

I awoke in the abandoned temple and saw the piles looming above me. They rattled and I heard once again the sharp rumbling sound. It was a sad song, sung with too much empathy. A dirge. I felt assaulted by the signs, warned. There was nothing to do but escape. The clock informed me that I'd been here for over a day, my nightmare had gone on and on. I was grateful simply to have awoken from that dream. The catalogue still lay on the bed. I grabbed it quickly, rushed out through the door and down the ramp, all the while checking left and right for the grandchild or Gustimoldo, expecting them to come in a car or jump out of a bush, but there was no one to stop me. Arriving at my car, I saw that it had stopped raining. The swallows overhead flew at an undefinable height, so I couldn't tell whether the rain would start again or let up. I placed the book in the passenger seat, started up the engine in neutral, but could not get it into first. Before I left, I was compelled to turn for a last look. The sight of the house struck me with disbelief that none of the neighbours had complained before. It must have been an industrial factory for such a long time, a workshop, and a warehouse of resignation. And inside, one was met with an uncertain provocation produced by a burning clarity. A plea to be an outlier. I decided then and there that no one else should ever enter that place. It must be destroyed. Whoever had made the signs must have felt the same. I put the car into first. With each meter that separated me from the house, I could feel a rising sensation of pleasure. I would wake from my wife's warm breath against my neck turned to condensation in the night. I would drink coffee and lay down between clean sheets. If Gustimoldo and the grandchild had been able to understand the joy of seeing one's child emerging from a period of sickness, of attending the funeral of someone trusted, of forgiving or of being forgiven, of enjoying a lamb steak with roasted root vegetables, the black signs would never have been written. I watched the fortress disappearing in the review mirror and began making plans for the following day. The first thing I would have to do would be to order a shipment of containers and a cleaning agency to scrub the place down, lock, stock and barrel. A non-Norwegian-speaking company would have to be tasked with melting down the signs, even if I had to pay extra for it. No one should ever know what I had seen. Gustimoldo was gone, the grandchild too. I would put an end to the history of the black signs. It was what I had to do.

II

Dear Gustimoldo

Rumour has it you were spotted surfing a tsunami wave of car parts, debris, and lampposts off the coast of Japan. Some say that you're now a leader of an innovation council in a banana republic somewhere near the border of Belize. Others have seen you on the pier at Ushuaia, staring at the fishing boats and seagulls—the gorillas of the sea—waiting for a casino to open up for a spot of cheap entertainment. Did you ever fulfil that dream of yours of moving to Richmond, Virginia to work part time at Philip Morris and the CIA?

I am writing to tell you that Grandma is dead. She was 108 years old. Now I am alone in the house, lost amongst the jutegnask. From my tribunal atop the stairway I can see a dragon-like pattern in the wooden panelling trailing the downward steps, inflicted when Grandma clawed the walls in her last attempt to defy the nursing home personnel. The scratch mark crosses a Josef Hoffmann ornament that is itself worthy of the Palais Stoclet before culminating in a precise Saarinen-like line at the doorway. On the inside of the mahogany door, Grandma concluded the line by carving an ambigram in classical Black Metal style. It is difficult from my vantage point to see it precisely, but if I knew Grandma at all, she wrote her motto "Let there be light!", readable from all angles. Even as she was dragged across the threshold of her childhood home, she maintained her devotion to art and artists until the end. Until her last, little, dusty breath, she was compelled toward creation. When the three male nurses were finally able to remove her to the nursing home—and a safe distance from the jutegnask—this battle ship of willpower began her slow sail away from the puddle of her body that lay upon the sickbed. The world's most renowned jutegnask collection out of her reach, her soul was depleted of its vigour and her days passed with 21-hour-long naps. The few hours that she was awake she spent humming the theme song to the TV-series "Professor Balthazar." The other residents, who were themselves already three quarters of the way into the valley of the shadow of death were able to rouse themselves enough to scuttle off to their rooms and lock the doors. Because her depletion wasn't total, Gustimoldo. Her will to inspire and to envision the future merely assumed more subtle forms. In the early afternoons, she would remove her dentures and stuff a handful of M&Ms in her mouth. She sat juggling the sweet rounds on her tongue, sucking the chocolate with a stream of rainbow coloured saliva on her chin. Then she would open her mouth widely and remove the polished peanuts, placing them in a dish. Grandma's home-sucked peanuts. She took great pleasure in these small moments of brilliance. When the afternoon visiting hour rolled around, she downed them all at once. As you may have already guessed, a queue had formed of devoted fans and fermented cultural personalities waiting to see her at the lunch hour. The staff told me that they came from near and far for the sole purpose of paying their last respects. After having observed one of these sessions, I realized that her visitors merely wished to be able to touch Grandma. Her limbs had become animate relics before she was even dead. Grandma allowed them to gently stroke the arteries in her neck and ankles as she gazed overbearingly down upon them. If she hadn't already been cremated by now, we may have been able to sell her lymph nodes for millions. Gustimoldo—you mustn't for a second believe that she ever stopped collecting jutegnask. Though there was hardly a speck of life left in her, her polaroid camera remained always on hand atop the nightstand.

And she would suddenly grab it and snap a photo of her visitors. Each one of them would then be required to sign the photos and dutifully record their metadata on the backside. When visiting hours were over, she stumbled from her bed to gather up her guests' forgotten newspapers and coffee grounds and would carefully scrutinize the chairs for bits of hair. From her deathbed, she managed to assemble well over 250 articles of jutegnask. However, the long distance to her house, her bulwark in life, finally drained her of strength once and for all. In the end, when she was no longer able to move, she took comfort in watching the TV-series "MacGyver," "The A-Team" and "Professor Balthazar", which I brought to her. She loved any edifying series in which the protagonists were required to overcome seemingly impossible odds through ingenuity. These stalwart characters replaced the artists, scientists and master architects of the twentieth century and their blind faith that the world was advancing like a torpedo shot linearly through time toward an ever-brighter target. Let there be light, Gustimoldo! When MacGyver blasted his way out of a bunker buried deep inside a mountain using only a teabag and a glass of pressed rhubarb, Grandma's shrill song of excited jubilation was enough to resurrect half of Oslo.

Grandma passed away uneasily one week ago. She was buried one honest, August day at Our Saviour's Cemetery. It was rumoured that there was a queue all the way down to the Akershus Fortress and that the city's public transport had to provide more services. The only thing I remember is the way the low sunbeams glared into my eyes through openings in the treetops, and that my black suit became a heated, sweating armour. I don't know how many hands I had to shake or grand words I had to endure, but the house was waiting for me and I needed only brook each and every degradation. Now I am here, sitting surrounded by her life's work, the most complete and defining jutegnask collection that has ever existed to date. "Grandma's sweet milk!" we often used to shout to ourselves. Together we have set our goal. Together we will carry it out. I look forward to getting started.

Come home, Gustimoldo.

Dear Gustimoldo

A brief follow-up letter with some practical tasks. I simply cannot wait, I am much too excited. Our first step is to draw up a proper index for every single object that can be found in the house. And by that, I mean down to the last specks of dust beneath the sofa cushions and the charred cheese remains on the stove—all is jutegnask.

The second step—auction them off.

When the earnings from the auctions begin to stream in—and I am truly looking forward to this—we can then put out a call for bids to produce the black signs. We will decide on the supplier best suited to our needs, send them our texts for the black signs and thus begin producing the signs. As the jutegnask disappears, the black signs will take its place. And then, Gustimoldo, we shall cover the land with black signs. However, in order to arrive at this goal, our days are filled with tasks. Remember, we must be completely devoted to our vision throughout these initial duties. It may well take a few months, perhaps years, but I am certain you will have returned by then. A working draft of our next steps is as follows:

* Convert the maid's quarters behind the kitchen into a workshop
* Purchase photo and computer equipment
* Assemble spacious workbenches and hooks for hanging up tools
* Put up shelves and racks for storing all outgoing jutegnask
* Send out a neighbourhood notification that we are undertaking a complete remodel and are

planning to install a swimming pool in the garden
* Receive bids for packaging, renovation work, mailing of jutegnask, etc.
* Tear out the parquet, wood panelling, retaining walls, and piping to free up space
* Build ramps for carrying out optimal operations without hindrances
* Consider investing in a hydraulic waste compressor

As you can see, we must make the interior organism of the house so dynamic that it serves as a workshop, a nucleus, a power factory—the house's every breath must be in line with our vision. As an inspiration, I have ordered a certified stamp of approval for jutegnask from a woodcarving shop in Stettin, Poland. It is comprised of a circular red rubber stamp with a handle of polished oak packaged in a custom wooden box. I myself sketched the drawing which the cutter used for the pattern. Beneath a stylized drawing of a house are the words, all in capitals: "AUTHORIZED JUTEGNASK FROM THE JUTEGNASK FOUNDATION, OSLO, NORWAY." We can gaze upon this expensively purchased stamp whenever we are exhausted and in need of motivation. It will be our golden calf, or to keep with the barn metaphors, our Trojan horse to suddenly take people by surprise where they cower behind their supposed safe walls.

This was the day's report.

Dear Gustimoldo

How should one write a sales description for Tomas Tran-
strömer's bloody band-aid or for Carmen Amaya's worn
out flamenco shoe? How should one talk about seven stolen packages of Sherbert from Pierre Klossowski? These
are the types of questions that now occupy my days.

Which leads us to a topic that we must clarify as soon as
possible—namely, how should we list the jutegnask at the
auctions? So many of the objects could be defined as rubbish, such as the holey socks of Danish artists and broth-
ers Asger Jorn and Jørgen Nash or the used cotton swabs
that Gertrude Stein left behind after her stay. How can we
convince our clients that the yellow dish gloves that are on
the kitchen counter are actually from the party that Mike
Kelley threw in honour of Öyvind Fahlström in Michigan?
Or that the coffee-soaked cube of sugar, which Grandma
wrapped painstakingly in a napkin, originates from a
meeting at a café with Yves Klein and Iris Clert in Paris?
There is a piece of soap on the writing desk which Arthur
Russell and Henry Flynt used to wash their hands at The
Kitchen. In the drawer is Jules Dassin's chequebook and
Gunvor Hofmo's pulverized liquorice lozenges. But how
should one market these objects, and how should one
prove their origins?

I hope the blood rushed to your head, Gustimoldo. Of
course, Grandma was a visionary here as well—how could
we ever believe otherwise? Every single bit of needed information is noted in meticulous detail on slips of paper
that are attached or glued to the back of the jutegnask. Her
entries also serve to place the objects in a historical context, to indicate the source and to help us significantly in

our sales descriptions for the auctions. Our chief challenge then, is to convert these bits of dry data into sales pitches. To this end, I have devised a solution which is rational, time-saving and edited down to the bare bones. This is only a draft, mind you, but keep in mind that we are talking about tens of thousands of jutegnask objects that must be registered, presented for auction, packaged, invoiced, declared, and posted. My proposed template is as follows:

1. Topic/Title
2. Year
3. Two to six lines describing the jutegnask and its origins.
4. Specification of media type, e.g., photo, dust, clothing, paper, metal, breadcrumbs, letters, clay, meat, pieces of hair, etc.
5. Simplified rating of object's condition. Here, I think that we should base our rating system on the international system used for online auctions. Good-, Good+, Good/Very Good, Very Good-, Very Good, Very Good+, Nearly Mint, Mint. If we were to follow the grading system used by auctioning houses such as Sotheby's and Christie's, with their detailed curator reports and sales histories, we would never attain our goal. We shall take the first option.
6. Certification number. Each object will receive a unique number proving that it is an authorized piece of jutegnask from Grandma's jutegnask collection. JG0001-
7. Three photographs (height, left, right)
8. A red stamp

By following this template to its every jot and tittle, we

shall be able to maintain a level of expertise and professionalism that will aid in reassuring our buyers. If we commit ourselves to speedy deliveries, package the jutegnask in a responsible manner and answer promptly to inquiries, I believe that we may quickly receive enough positive feedback to be classifiable as a PowerSeller. Alternatively, we could choose to go through an established auction house. But to be honest, Gustimoldo, I'm not very eager to involve outsiders. It isn't because 20% of the winnings disappear into their pockets, because this is a reasonable commission. Rather, just between you and me, there are simply too many objects in Grandma's jutegnask collection that cross far beyond a line. Some of the jutegnask are stolen goods and others indicate low morals. Who would think of scooping up bits of Franz Masereel's shattered kneecap in a handkerchief as he lay unconscious following a bicycle accident along the banks of the Rhone in Avignon? Grandma. This is why I believe it would be best for us to maintain control at all levels of the process.

Yesterday was an encouraging day. I initiated a trial auction to see how much control we could keep over the timing, and also how well my classification template would hold up. A few days ago, I prepared the grey piece of meat that has been stored in the deep freezer for so many years. Do you remember that cut that Grandma used to threaten us with that we would have to eat if we didn't finish the over-boiled cod that lay on our plates? We would then shovel down the cod, even if we only preferred "yellow fish", because we never wanted that freezer to be opened. I found out from Grandma's attached note that the cut of meat came from a show that Hermann Nitsch and his ensemble "Orgy Mystery Theatre" performed in Bayreuth in 1964. The sales description that I wrote was thus:

HERMANN NITSCH'S LEG OF LAMB (1964)

Leg of lamb of Swiss biodynamic origin. Used in the "Orgy Mystery Theatre" performance in Bayreuth, Germany on October 23, 1964.

Lamb meat
VG- (Demeter-label missing)
JG0001

I set the auction time to seven days and the starting price at 15 dollars. At the bottom of the description, I wrote "Authorized Jutegnask from the Jutegnask Foundation, Oslo, Norway" as the concluding remarks. After a few hours, questions from interested purchasers began trickling in. The inbox was filled to the rim, and I worked to continuously delete the emails. I was worried that the whole thing might develop into an all-encompassing debate about authenticity and grading systems. To my surprise, simply mentioning Grandma's name and my relationship as kin proved to be a more than satisfactory answer. The jutegnask was thereby verified, and no more questions were asked. The rumour that the world's leading jutegnask collection might be auctioned off spread faster than we ever could have imagined. One could truly feel the reverence expressed for Grandma and her life's work. Gustimoldo—after 28 hours, the highest bid on the leg of lamb is now at 6,000 dollars and climbing with each hour. Hermes, the god of bidding, has gone absolutely bananas.

People are—just as we have always known—crazy for jutegnask.

See you soon, Gustimoldo.

Dear Gustimoldo

A short status update on the plans. The construction work is going well. The supporting walls of the house, the doors, recessed shelves, various trimmings and unusable wood panelling have all been removed and disposed of. I have decided to hold off on tearing out the parquet and removing pipes until we know whether more space is needed. I have no idea how much storage space is required for a million signs. Do you? The maid's quarters have been emptied and converted into a workshop. It was filled with jutegnask, but I moved all of that into the kitchen until further notice. The technical equipment has been purchased and hooked up, and I have installed spacious workbenches. Gustimoldo, I don't wish to bore you with details in a letter, but there is one thing I must mention. Yesterday, a construction company came by and put up a 4 x 4 metre aluminium ramp leading up to the veranda in the back garden. This is the best solution to our logistical challenges, I think. The overgrown garden will hide our import of goods from our neighbour's prying eyes. They all think we're putting in a swimming pool. Now all that's left is to simply roll in pallet after pallet of black signs. In fact, I need to write that on my shopping list: one pallet truck.

In my last letter I indicated a real sphinx of a challenge which requires the most delicate, clarifying touch. In our sales descriptions, we promote the collection as the most widely acknowledged, leading, complete and generation-defining jutegnask collection on earth. Strong words indeed. Has it ever occurred to you that only two people in the entire world actually know what jutegnask means? I think we must come up with a definition, as many potential bidders will certainly require an explanation. If we don't, we will risk that the jutegnask may be falsely perceived and compared with everyday collector's items, souvenirs, trinkets, relics, memorabilia, curios, baubles and mul- tiples—some kind of distant relative to arts and crafts. I went back over your notes to review the origins of the word jutegnask. I thought we had just pulled the word out of thin air, but in the archives I discovered some of your curled up notes showing that you'd spent time considering the word's meaning and all that we would inherit from Grandma. Your handwriting was not difficult to read.

> *Jutegnask is gaining recognition in the western world... Its growth can be attributed to the explo- sive increase in people within the system who be- lieve that art in a broad sense (music, design, cu- linary art, sports, architecture, etc.) and its artists are able to realize the dreams of every person. For this reason, the art constitutes a proportionally large portion of their inner mental lives... Though the majority have realized that they themselves are not artists, neither in this life or in the next, they have nonetheless become completely dependent on art. Artists have now been tasked with constructing peoples' souls, their marrow and meaning—their leitmotifs—and this has led to a previously unrec- ognised lust after art in all its forms. Whether it's a handshake from a crime writer or the cigarette butt that your favourite guitarist stamps out back- stage before a concert. Whoever is not in close prox- imity to art in today's society is considered soulless, forever lost, as on a ghost ship traversing the high seas with no possibility of harbour unless one can find the mode of expression necessary to come in to land... To be with Jutegnask is all we ask.*

Among other files in the archives, I found more of your scribbled notes providing an additional, more clear definition:

> *Jutegnask is an aesthetic epiphenomenon. Jutegnask are animate art relics that linger in the indefinable realm between art and rubbish. Non-art-art = jutegnask. The name refers to all objects within the artistic production which are not defined as artwork by the artist himself. They are not written in an official list of works, but are catalogued by a golden pen in an alternative directory that is not controlled by any artist, museum director or gallery owner... Jutegnask are the traces of the artist or a work of art and are inextricably linked to it... If the artist is pure, nourishing and life-giving, then all objects surrounding the artist glow and have their own power... Jutegnask touches on a leprosy, an illness, a longing of our contemporary self-worth. It is therefore of utmost relevance to collect jutegnask.*

Gustimoldo, I don't think you saw any difference between a Norwegian outhouse and Duchamp, but the third note that I am holding is also covered with your writing. And here, we are finally led to your thoughts regarding the connections that jutegnask has in the historical context of art and ideas.

You never cease to amaze me.

> *... jutegnask is simply the realisation of what was prophesied by Duchamp's readymades, Luigi Russolo's theories of noise, Cage's all-sound principles, pop art's appropriation techniques, and the Fluxus Movement's idiotic smirk: that everything is art,*

and anyone can be an artist. We have progressed by leaps and bounds toward a consciousness in which the distinction between art and everyday life has been abolished for good. Jutegnask is the ultimate fulfilment of the pragmatist's prediction that art is experience and experience is art. A fundamentally democratic reality has the world in its grip, and anything and everything that falls within the realm of our sensory reality has an equal right to be noticed.

Such large words aside, by far the best explanation of jutegnask is what you once told me in passing when we were in the fresh produce section of the supermarket. You held up a red apple and said, so mildly:

Although Shakespeare penned thousands of wingéd stanzas which we quote with utmost devotion, it was the words such as "How much do these apples cost?" and "What shall we eat for supper?" that passed through his mouth more often. A jutegnask collection is comprised of such sentences.

The way I see it, the field that jutegnask spans is nearly incomprehensible. Jutegnask includes an invitation to the opening of Dieter Roth's exhibition at Kurt Kalb's gallery in Vienna, which is printed with a different motif than the one on the exhibition poster, or which includes a personally penned inscription from the artist on the back. An sms sent from Kjell Askildsen, informing his wife that he refuses to go to the seafood restaurant again today, is jutegnask. It's the same with Valerie Export's tangled signature on a taxi receipt from Rotterdam. I would also include a half empty Alt beer bottle consumed in Kraftwerk's Kling Klang studio, which Grandma snatched and took with her, within the lines of definition. Karl Ove Knausgård's Swedish prescription for bipolar eczema cream, is jutegnask. Robert Musil's bag with a shrimp shell from a picnic in Frankfurt or an audio tape recording of Chris Cutler verbally abusing Kenneth Goldsmith, is clearly jutegnask. So is Virginia Woolf's swimming cap. A photo of Chris Marker, on which someone has written "nomisuke"—big drinker in Japanese—on his forehead after a boozy evening in Tokyo with Wim Wenders and Grandma, is clearly in. I would call Claudia Cardinale's ankle bandage, containing strings of wool lint from her sock, jutegnask. A broken jack cable used by Billy Klüver on "9 Evenings: Theatre and Engineering" at the Armory in New York is, by definition, jutegnask. Also acceptable is a plastic mask of Kjartan Slettemark's face, which Grandma swiped after his performance with Lasse Marhaug in Landmark in 2006. A letter from Winston Churchill to Grandma, in which he writes that "his beard is laughing" after he was awarded the Nobel Prize in literature in 1953 for his memoir, and that he is "really looking forward" to meeting Grandma in Oslo, is also jutegnask. Jean Dubuffet's homemade walnut pesto and Bibi Andersson's half empty bottle of applejuice from Kivik, is jutegnask. A video clip of Liam Gillick drunkenly punching Tom McCarthy while claiming that Metronome Press is a poor imitation of Girodias' publishing house, Olympia Press, is jutegnask. Olaf Bull's French manual for enema—paid for with money he earned giving Norwegian lessons to James Joyce in Paris—is well within the margins. The orange thermos with liquorice tea that Richard Long and Grandma took with them on their walking tour when making his landscape art through Dartmoor, is jutegnask. Inger Sitter and Carl Nesjar's marriage papers and Pauline Olivero's half empty asthma inhaler are excellent examples. That which distinguishes jutegnask from accepted artwork is that jutegnask is not included in any official register, list of works or catalogue. The system is based on trust, grassroots enthusiasm and a shared respect of sentimental value. There are millions of jutegnask collections spread throughout the world today, but they exist far outside the realm of academic discipline and artistic circles. Each and every patron of jutegnask creates his own collection and exhibition, his own private *Wunderkammer* or curiosity cabinet, if you will, taking care to keep it tucked away from the public eye. Today, no one knows for certain just how much jutegnask exists, or when this tradition began, but based on my humble experience, there are an alarming number of collectors following in Grandma's footsteps. But in the midst of this uncertain and prevailing chaos, one fact remains solidly written in stone: Grandma is, by far, the undisputed pioneer and authority within the field of jutegnask.

Which makes us, Gustimoldo, the owners of the world's largest jutegnask collection. Or rather—we are the chairmen, representatives, managers, administrators, technical conservators, directors, curators, librarians, caretakers and receptionists for the world's most comprehensive private jutegnask foundation. It's a pity that the mission statement indicates that everything in stock must be sold to finance the black signs.

This is probably not what the donor had in mind.

My friend and mentor—it is lonely to be the only full time employee in the jutegnask foundation.

Come home.
Come forth.

Dear Gustimoldo

As I catalogue object after object of jutegnask, I am sitting in the maid's quarters thinking about the donor and the infernal determination that underlies her collection. Have you ever stopped to think about who Grandma was exactly, besides being the somewhat involuntary investor of the black signs? Was she a force, an obsession, a will or a person? I do not know. Grandma made her entry into the world of art in 1906. She was four years old. Her family went on a bathing holiday in Warnemünde, where two young men, Ernst Ludwig Kirchner and Karl Schmidt-Rottluft, politely asked her father whether they could paint a portrait of his daughter. Their usual child model, Fränzi, was unfortunately sick with rubella. The two artists had noticed Grandma earlier that day as she stood on the water's edge trying to catch the waves. The scene stirred their curiosity so greatly that they followed the family and summoned their courage for many hours before daring to ask permission. More than 14 oil paintings were composed that afternoon. Schmidt-Rottluff and Kirchner couldn't get enough of their favourite new model. Grandma posed wrapped in a white fur coat slung across her bathing suit. Her lips were coloured with bright red lipstick, but otherwise no makeup was necessary. It would have been a crime, indeed to rub anything else into that vibrant summer skin which glowed beneath her salt-bleached hair. Grandma wore an expression in which her lower lip pushed her upper lip outwards while her eyes gazed pensively downward. This became her trademark expression and would be interpreted by thousands of artists for the next hundred and four years. Even though Schmidt-Rottluff and Kirchner conveyed Grandma in the typical Brücke-mode, employing strong, dirty colours, flat abstractions and an obvious outline made with quick strokes, I have never seen such strength of character bursting from a person. A critic at the *Süddeutsche Zeitung* who had viewed the paintings at an exhibition at the Pinakothek der Moderne in Munich, described Grandma's audacious will for life as a hand breaking out of the canvas. Apparently, he had run sprinting out of the museum and subsequently refused to report on the exhibition. "One hundred times more solid than Fränzi or Marsella," Kirchner told her father when he came to pick up his daughter. He noticed that Grandma had been treated as an equal by the artists. She could converse for hours about cultural politics, the publishing industry's decline and the tendency of the film media to allow for a new, universal language that might revolutionize communication between individuals. Even worse was the fact that, in the course of a single day, she had learned to outdrink the Brücke circle and had developed a strong desire for anything made from the sylvan grapes.

She was four years old.

Since that day in Warnemünde, Grandma and art became inseparable. People said that Grandma was a trained artist, though I never witnessed a single confirmation to this fact. Some said that she studied under Christian Krohg at the State Art Academy in 1920 and that she showed a painting at a student exhibition the following year. An older man who I chatted with at one of Grandma's countless parties told me that he had been present at the exhibition in 1921. He laughed heartily when I asked about Grandma's painting because it was the only work that he was unable to see at the exhibit. He then assured me that he had truly tried to catch a glimpse of it but Grandma had always been in the way of the painting the entire evening.

Not physically, of course, because she ran around talking to everyone and about everything as usual, but even when she was out on the dance floor or holding down a conversation in the opposite corner of the room, yes even when she was in the restroom, Grandma blocked the view of her painting with her laughter, her lustre, her profane movements or a flick of her skirt. If such reasons contributed to one not being able to call Grandma an artist, then she was at least allowed to be given diffuse titles for the rest of her life, such as provocateur, soulmate, inspirer, visionary, giver of meaning, consultant, curator, muse, lover, juror, trendsetter, mentor.

She was Grandma.

It is difficult to imagine that this woman—who clapped for joy whenever MacGyver managed to surf a wave of boiling lava from out of an irritable volcano with the help of some walnuts and baking soda mixed in a thermos—had received more than 23 degrees in the last 90 years. She belonged to one of the first cohorts at the Bauhaus in Weimar and studied dance under Martha Graham in New York in the 1930s. She attended all of the summer courses in Darmstadt and took private lessons in composition from Helmut Lachenmann in Stuttgart in the 1980s. She was named honorary professor in philosophy at Harvard in 1965 and took a corresponding doctorate at the Sorbonne in the 1990s, under the supervision of Derrida. M.C. Richards, Charles Olson and Willem de Kooning were her instructors of literature and fine arts during her time spent at the Black Mountain College in North Carolina. At the age of 89, she was accepted at the Dresden Academy of Fine Arts where she studied under Gerard Richter while simultaneously pursuing her curatorial masters at the Stockholm Konstfack college of arts, crafts and design with her thesis: *Artists Are my Raw Material*. And this is only a fraction of her educational history, Gustimoldo. There are drawers filled to the brim with diplomas and transcripts. One would think from this that Grandma sat locked in reading rooms or at a desk most of the time, but I've never seen her perform an honest day's work. It was enough that she was simply present, alive and doing what she did. Harbouring a deep fear of losing her to other countries, the powers that be in Norway set up a salary for her. This they managed to justify with the fact that Grandma was an important promoter and ambassador on behalf of Norwegian culture. At a lutefisk party in 1988, Cy Twombly succinctly defined Grandma as he praised her to a Norwegian journalist: "She's like... yeah, you know... like Mozart, just without the classical music."

And now I am sitting here in her house, selling off her life's work to the highest bidder.

BRUCE NAUMAN'S COPY OF SAMUEL BECKETT'S LE DÉPEUPLEUR (1984)

The book is a first edition copy of Les Éditions de Minuit published in 1970. The inscription to Grandma on the back reads: "In gratitude for giving me the strength to create 'Room with My Soul Left Out, Room That Does Not Care'. Hope to see you at Leo's later this week. Kisses, Bruce."

Bound book
NM
JG0027

ALBERT AYLER'S BEARD TRIMMINGS (1962)

Transparent plastic bag with 73 grams of Albert Ayler's beard trimmings. From the time that Grandma shaved Ayler, on the day before he recorded his debut album *Something Different!!!!* in Bird Note's studio in Stockholm.

Black and white discarded hair
VG-
JG0028

JEFF KOON'S MOON BOOTS (2004)

Purple moon boots, size 45. From Koon's visit to Norway in 2004 in conjunction with his retrospective exhibit at The Astrup Fearnley Museum of Modern Art. Grandma bought the boots for him because the poor guy only brought a pair of thin canvas shoes with him to Oslo and was surprised by the early snowfall. Paid for with Hans Rasmus Astrup's credit card.

Polyester/plastic
NM
JG0029

HALLDÓR LAXNESS' RAZOR BLADE (1971)

Gillette razor blade that was used to neuter suckling pigs at Laxness' farm on Mosfell in Iceland. Laxness took Grandma on a tour of his childhood home, including the barn, and she used the opportunity to secretly confiscate the razor blade that lay in the bloody sawdust and to hide it in her green Dent mint tin.

Metal
VG+ (rust and blood)
JG0030

ULAY'S COPY OF BARIŞ MANÇO' 2023 (1976)

Turkish LP-album given in gratitude to Grandma for her help to Mike Steiner and Ulay by distracting the guards at the Neue Nationalgalerie in Berlin as they stole Carl Spitzweg's "The Poor Poet" in 1976. Grandma was presented with the gift during dinner at the Turkish family's home in Kreuzberg, where Ulay hung up the stolen painting on the wall before turning himself into the police.

Vinyl with cardboard cover
VG- (a small scratch on the outer grooves of side B)
JG0031

FÉLIX FÉNÉONS USED MILK CARTON (1929)

Empty milk carton from the French supplier Lactalis. Written on the side is an unpublished, three-line novella by Félix Fénéon dedicated to Grandma: "An old woman, on exiting a car in Rue Augustin, grabbed hold of the car door to steady herself. The car door proceeded to slam against her leg, severing the artery in her left ankle. As she bled to death, she protested: 'I was trying to take a stand.'"

Cardboard
VG- (unpleasant odour)
JG0032

LETTER FROM GEORGE BATAILLE (1961)

Two page long handwritten letter containing an outburst against Foucault and his *Madness and Civilization*. His clos-

ing remarks state: "That son of an ape looks like a cross between Yul Brynner and a dildo with legs."

A4-page of paper
G- (tears in upper right corner and the pages are partially
bleached by the sun)
JG0033

WALTER RUTTMAN'S STONE (1928)

A flat skipping stone grabbed from the bottom of the Spree
by Walter Ruttman. A brown rubber band around the stone
holds in place a folded piece of paper with the words: "Thank
you for the rewarding stroll through Berlin together with
Bruno Taut. It served to arouse my curiosity in this enchanting city once more. Walt."

Stone, paper, rubber band
VG
JG0034

TABLE SCRAPS FROM AN EVENING OF CABBAGE AND LAMB STEW WITH CARL NESJAR, ERLING VIKSJØ, PABLO PICASSO AND GRANDMA (1953)

Cooked in Picasso's studio kitchenette in Paris where the
quartet discussed their possible participation in decorating
the new government quarter in Oslo. Picasso became angry
and lashed out at Nesjar for putting the pepper corns freely
into the pan instead of adding them from the shaker. This action did not sit well with Picasso.

Bits of lamb leg, dried cabbage and pepper corns
VG-
JG0035

HANNAH HÖCH'S OVEN MITTS (1925)

The oven mitts were given in gratitude to Grandma for
having driven, together with Til Brugman, some of Höch's

materials back to Berlin after a solo exhibition in Amsterdam. Grandma has noted that one can see the outline of the painting "Die Journalisten" in certain unconscious creases in the fabric and that this fact is no mere coincidence.

Cotton
G+ (burn marks throughout several layers, limited functionality)
JG0036

EXCHANGE OF LETTERS BETWEEN ROY ANDERSON, TERRENCE MALICK AND GRANDMA (1981)

39 pages of correspondence between Roy Anderson, Terrence Malick and Grandma on the topics of criticism, performance anxiety and depression. Anderson is critical that Malick uses movie stars such as Richard Gere and Martin Sheen to play the main characters in his films and suggests that he employ amateur actors instead. The eighth letter contains a jovial description of a meeting at MoMA in 2004, where Malick writes to Grandma that Anderson behaved like "a coffee deprived hick art historian."

Paper
VG+
JG0037

BRIAN JONES' MOROCCAN DRUM (1968)

The drum was a gift to Grandma from Brian for brilliantly fulfilling her role as a roadie for "The Master Musicians of Jajoukas" Scandinavia tour in 1968. He thanks Grandma that she and Brion Gysin introduced him to the village of Jajouka in 1965 and, across the skin of the drum, he has written: "To my blackbird. Paul and William send their greetings."

Wood, leather
VG
JG0038

AGNAR MYKLE'S BALLAST PLANT (1971)

Brought back in a handbag after a trip to Morocco in 1971. When he planted it, an unknown *antropochor* spread, causing the extermination of all berry plants in the Mykle's residential area in Asker. To this day, no berries grow in the area.

Green plant
VG+ (grows heartily in a pot)
JG0039

LETTER FROM NADIA BOULANGER (1955)

Letter from Boulanger in which Grandma is reprimanded for having disturbed Piazzolla's and Boulez' studies with her corrupt and salacious lifestyle. "Keep an arms length from my other pupils, you vile harlot. Yours Nadia."

Paper
G+ (clear fold marks)
JG0040

EILEEN GRAY'S LIP BALM WITH HEATHER NECTAR FLAVOUR (1929)

During a violent quarrel between Jean Badovicis and Gray, Grandma was hit by a plastic tube of lip balm. This she quickly smuggled into her purse before Gray came over to Grandma and blew innocently on the blue mark left on her forehead from the blow.

Lip balm, plastic
VG- (half full)
JG0041

SIGNED COPY OF ARTUR LUNDKVIST'S THE TALKING TREE (1960)

The book, with cover art by Öyvind Fahlstrøm, contains a handwritten dedication on the inside flap: "Forget about Maria—you are my open-eyed dream, my late autumn homestead."

Pocketbook
VG- (watermark on front cover)
JG0042

GLASS FROM BLACK MOUNTAIN COLLEGE (1953)

A 2 dl water glass from the cafeteria at Black Mountain College in Asheville, North Carolina. Grandma took it after a common meal in the cafeteria. She writes on an accompanying note that there is a large chance that Anni Albers and Buckminster Fuller have both drunk from the glass.

Clear glass with fingerprints
NM- (calcium buildup on the glass)
JG0043

STIG SÆTERBAKKEN'S EMPTY WHISKY GLASS (2008)

Originating from the time that Grandma and Sæterbakken travelled to Islay on the west coast of Scotland. The aim of their trip was to conduct hands-on research for an article that he was writing about whisky for the magazine *Vinduet*. At Duffies Whisky Bar in Bowmore, Grandma outdrank Sæterbakken until he lay unconscious, at which point she ransacked his limp body for jutegnask items, among them Sæterbakken's empty glass with lip and fingerprints, which she later packaged in bubble wrap.

Glass
VG+ (small chip in the upper rim)
JG0044

Dear Gustimoldo

Still no sign of you, so I must attempt to summon you by other means.

Your consistent misperception of reality laid the basis for a richer existence. Like when you believed that The Beatles' "Hey Jude" was a song about the Holocaust which urged Jews not to go around so sad all the time. How was it exactly that you were able to fit the chorus—"Na, na, na nananana, nananana"—into your theory? A broken arm was synonymous with having it completely ripped off. I once watched from a distance as you stood spitting straight up into the air. When saliva landed on your shoulder, you cursed the rain and proceeded to deliver a loud sermon about the challenges of climate change in Norway. You claimed that only outcasts from the main European continent would have been forced to settle down in such a godforsaken place, a weak genetic history that continues to plague us. There were other times though, when your constant misunderstandings led to less charming episodes. Such as when you insisted that the girl who worked at the coffee bar was fervently in love with you because she swirled a heart in the foam of your cappuccino. The entire affair ended with you practically moving in to the café, consuming coffee until you trembled with caffeine, and imagined she was implying her desire to give you a hand job when rubbing down the foam wand with a cloth. You leapt over the bar.

A richer existence.

I am sitting on Grandma's green flannel sofa with golden tassels and seams and have a pocket edition of Paulo Coelho's *Veronika Decides to Die* in my hands. The blurbs on the first page draw the reader in. "Superb portrayal of madness! Buy this book!"—Cathrine Krøger Hammerstrøm, *Dagbladet*. "This is the best book I have ever read. — Sinéad O'Connor." You received the Coehlo book from a well-meaning nurse who felt truly sorry for you and imagined that the book might help to prevent your soul from distortion. I imagine you offering polite thanks for the book, nodding and bowing exaggeratedly, before darting off home and going at it with your red pen. Did you view this book as an exercise in rhetoric and derision—an invitation to grind your axe? In the flap of *Veronika Decides to Die*, you have written in large letters:

NOLI ME TANGERE

Don't touch me.

A plea?

After only a few pages, you are in full Gustimoldo-mode.

> *We must strive towards positive nihilism. That which eradicates contradictions.*

And then a character assassination:

MISUNDERSTOOD HUMANISM

Underlined twice in red.

I browse through the book and feel each page, let them flap past my thumb and pick at your dog-ears. In the beginning, every single page was folded, showing your restlessness. In some places you folded the same edge multiple times so that the paper became limp and lost its texture. In other places, you have forgotten yourself, all but disappeared, reading dozens of pages before another dog-ear pops up again. A little respite from yourself. I imagine to myself that each fold in the book, each visible crease corresponds to some place on your body. A pair of nervous creases are the worry lines on your forehead. A particular dog-eared flap reminds me of the bunch of skin between your wrist and palm. A corner of repeated, harsh folds is like the similar folds of skin around your waist, where purplish stretch marks crisscross your horizontal love handles.

In the back of the book, you have once again attached one of your countless newspaper clippings. I remember this, one of your favourites. The image is from a rape case in China where the victim escaped by biting off the perpetrator's tongue during the assault. She ran to her freedom with a bit of tongue in her cheek. The offender took to hiding in a barn outside the village for fear the police would wait for him at the nearest hospital. The infection in his wound got worse and the pain became unbearable. He was forced to seek out a doctor, which led to his arrest. On the right in the photo is the lightly sedated culprit, mouth open to reveal a slanted tongue stump. The victim is sitting next to him. She has a hood on so as not to be recognized and is holding up a small plastic bag containing a piece of tongue. With her free hand, she is gesturing at her assailant, who with a sweep of her hand becomes a living trophy. Behind both of them, four senior government officials in uniform are posing proudly. The all-enveloping flash makes the photograph appear uncomfortably bright. Whoever looks at the photo also feels like the camera just flashed in their eyes. Was it because you could identify with the perpetrator, Gustimoldo, that you cut out this article? No tongue to speak with and hands bound behind your back, or was it the unwavering dispensation of guilt that drew you? I place the article back in the book. A folded corner on a page calls to mind the folds of the thin skin behind your ear, the skin between your fingers. In one deep crease, I picture the lines on your neck, visible only when you shaved, which was seldom. So many pages, so many red marks, and countless folds.

I must summon you in other ways.

As I expected, you have sketched out one of your signature drawings on a blank page at the back of the book. Your version of the Sisyphus myth. In strokes of red, green and black—institutional colours—we see Sisyphus descending from the mountain to fetch his stone yet again. You are not one bit interested in portraying Sisyphus' curse or eternal toil. Instead, you are occupied by what is going on in his secret lair on the back side of the mountain. Sisyphus is happily telling himself "Not even the gods can find me here." In this small room inside the mountain, complete with bed, TV, prostitute and refrigerator, he has stored a *pata negra* ham and a bottle of hard alcohol. Each time he saunters down the mountain, Sisyphus pauses for a feast which is followed by a long nap in his freshly changed bed. He falls asleep with his mouth in a sneer. Then he wakes up to go roll a bit of stone up the hill.

Gustimoldo—you bring me breezes of happiness, but gales of depression. You are Rahula, Buddha's only son, abandoned as a suckling when his father decided to venture out and seek enlightenment. Only you, the earthbound, remained to hold an eternal home-alone party.

I will take care of your book until you've returned.

Dear Gustimoldo

You would have been proud of me today. I get dizzy just thinking about how much work I've completed in the last few hours. I awoke at sunrise, put on a full pot of coffee and showered. My breakfast consisted, as do each of my meals, of natural yoghurt, my single source of nutrition aside from coffee. Besides the fact that yoghurt purifies the body, I am able to save at least one hour each day in the time it would take to prepare and clean up a meal and to visit the toilet. In the cold cellar, I have stored a dozen enormous canisters of yoghurt which can keep me alive for many months. Following my breakfast, I photographed, catalogued and packaged 117 pieces of jutegnask. The loft became much more spacious after this task. A skylight that I have never noticed before became visible, providing the room with natural lighting. I'm flirting with the idea of tackling another round of jutegnask after lunch with a goal of 250 entries in just one day. The only thing keeping me from it is the heat. Oslo is in the grips of a last, late summer heat wave, so I will have to see how much I am able to accomplish. In addition, the air in the attic is bad, there is so much jutegnask that hasn't been touched since it was collected and stored by Grandma. The dust is thickly layered and many items have rotted. On the more positive side, I am happy to report that the house seems to in- and exhale more or less in rhythm with our vision. The conversion of the maid's quarters into a workshop has been a success. Now that the doorway and fittings have been removed, it really feels like I am living in a factory—everything runs on wheels. I roll the packaged jutegnask out when I'm done and place it along the storage shelves. The first auctions will soon conclude and I will be able to mail the jutegnask and send it out of the house.

My happiness begins to increase.

There's no getting around it, here's the fly in the ointment. As the auctions draw to a close, the second phase begins. The earnings will enable our production of the black signs. The workload will expand to include orders, proofs, logistics and tightly monitored management of the entire project. At the same time, one must continue to clean, register and auction off the jutegnask. The mere task of coordinating the shipments of jutegnask with the shipping company is a part-time job in itself. As you might imagine, it would be nice if you could be here when the second phase begins. I cannot hire a substitute: this is *our* task.

Gustimoldo, we have to talk.

Dear Gustimoldo

You are a person who takes a long time to love.

When your family moved into the neighbourhood, it wasn't long before you were dubbed "Christ" by the locals. You received that moniker after you were bullied by some older boys for your appearance, and you screamed back at them that it wasn't your fault you had been born one year too soon. And no one questioned whether this had to do with original sin or genetic disposition, but everyone took it for granted that it was probably a little of both.

From the first moment I crossed the threshold to your family's apartment—where your mother always lounged in the bathtub; where your little sister sat strapped into her high chair watching old recordings of "Casino" with Halvor Flatland on a looped, three-hour video cassette; where I was assaulted by the damp odour of your three-legged Handicat, thanks to his mistaking the humidifier as his litter box; where your father stood frying noisette potatoes in the kitchen—I surrendered to you, Gustimoldo. I remember you described your childhood thus:

> I shall not pass judgement upon myself, God shall decide on the day of judgement. However, with a childhood such as mine, I have every right to be brain dead.

Maybe you were born one year too early. Your face is shaped as though God, in the last second, realized that there weren't enough chromosomes to go around, but didn't have enough time to fix the counting error. Your chin and forehead were a membrane of pastry-thin skin, stretched out over the bones, like a newly pitched circus tent across your skull, which was crowned with a shaggy mop of brown hair. Your translucent skin could be attributed to the case of vodka that your mother had hidden behind the humidifier during her pregnancy. After nine months of swimming in vodka-laced amniotic fluid, your skin was so dissolved that it was a miracle it didn't tear immediately. Your large white front teeth rested permanently in your lower lip. As if you were constantly ready to spit out a dirty word starting with the letter f. Your explanation for this was that you had knocked out your front teeth as a three year old, and in an effort to hide the incident from your mother, your father had quickly shoved two squares of chewing gum into the bloody gaps. These squares soon hardened within the gums and became your enlarged incisors. I imagined that the general advisory committee behind your facial structure must have consisted of chemicals, pollutants and unsaturated fats. For over 15 years, you had an unofficial agreement with the woman who owned the corner kiosk. Because you never received pocket money to buy sweets for yourself, you asked whether you could be allowed to take the dust that was left over in the candy drawer, which she was planning to throw out in any case. After a long period, the woman collected a large plastic bag full of candy dust which you could then pick up each first Sunday of the month. You ate candy dust with a spoon until you were an adult. But most of all, I believe that your face was shaped by the thoughts you had about yourself. Although you were on welfare for your entire life, never even finished high school, and your circle of acquaintances only surpassed mine by a few peripheral Internet-friends from Canada, in your own self perception you were of more worth than Napoleon, Socrates or Kennedy—you were heir to a throne in a royal lineage that deserved to rule. You were an amateur-omniscient, the earnest everyman with answers to all of life's questions, who positions himself on the right, on the left and in the radical centre, and who is always in the right wherever he may be located. Because, compared to Socrates and that gang, you had the Internet and a 10 dollar USB stick attached to your key ring that contained more knowledge than they could ever read throughout their entire life. Gustimoldo: you were that petit-nihilist who revelled in the dark, but who shrieked in alarm if anything happened to you, even if it was just a tiny cut on your finger.

Can you hear me?

I can remember one typical day in the Gustimoldo-household. Your mother was soaking in the yellow bathtub with the door opened, intently leafing through gossip magazines while shouting commands at you and your father. She was an aristocratic, bitter actress and model who had been rejected at every Fassbinder audition and had never been cast in a film. In the 1980s, she had been the mistress of one of the founders of the clothing chain Bik Bok and could talk for hours about the house parties where Per Spook himself had been present. The highpoint of her career came when she outperformed Rita Westvik in an audition, landing the role of a mysterious woman who rode about on a white horse in one of Casino Steel's music videos. Her aristocratic face and stick-thin body didn't correspond well to the sack, or pouch, of her stomach which protruded from beneath her ribs. Above her stomach hung what may earlier have been called breasts, but which had now turned into something that is physiologically termed teats. She was no longer occupied so much with Fassbinder and Spook rather, she was ashamed of her body after giving birth to you and your little sister, and had now dedicated her life to continuously bathing in all varieties of oils and products designed to remove stretch marks. When she would refill the tub with boiling water, the steam turned the apartment into a house of aromas, featuring the world's spectrum of tax-free perfumes and Handicat's eternal bewilderment. We who would be playing video games in the room would start choking. Do you remember that smell? And just when we thought the context for playing Super Mario couldn't get any worse, a peculiar, butter-thick stench from the kitchen would waft out, blending itself together with the rose-piss smell. From the bathtub, your mother would start sniffing and saying to herself: "Noisettes? What? Noisettes!" Your father would be standing in the kitchen, preparing oven-baked broccoli with hollandaise sauce and noisette potatoes. This last item was a constant component of every meal in your home. Your mother was possessed with a basic belief that noisettes belonged only in the most cultivated homes and at palace parties, a misperception stemming from an advertising campaign she once watched while suffering withdrawal in 1984. Any item on one's plate was elevated to a noble standard as long as noisettes were included in the dish. The murmurs from the bathtub were soon after followed with an exaggeratedly syrupy question: "Dearest, are we having noisettes again today?" Yes, you would be having noisettes, and your childhood home would, for a rare moment, be in a state of complete harmony. After dinner your mother went straight to bed. She didn't touch the broccoli, but the potent combination of having consumed a large portion of noisettes and soaking in the tub all day long was apparently quite exhausting. Your father would carry her into the bedroom, dry off her puckered skin, and lay her gently down onto the bed. He would then return to the living room, unstrap the belt that held your little sister in place, and take her into her mother for her last goodnight kiss. The ritual brought to mind a dictator who hasn't seen his firstborn for many months due to war raging on the front. In your mother's defence, your father would say: "She's had a rough time, she has, so many things have destroyed her, so many things have gone wrong. It hasn't been easy for her. She was talented. No, it hasn't been easy for her, certainly not." Any concern for your wellbeing, Gustimoldo, was somehow omitted from this lament.

Do I err to describe your father as a sausage-maker from Fredrikstad who became the proprietor of the Cai Bau religious headquarters in Norway? While on travels to Brazil in the 1980s, he bought the Cai Bau agency for Norway, a religion that melts down all of the world's faiths into a single clump, with 2.5 million followers worldwide. "And the numbers get bigger each year, you know!" He would then start in on the Italian priest Don Bosco's vision that the Kingdom of the Third Millennium would one day come to appear between the 15th and 20th latitudes, which is where Brasília and its Sunrise Valley are located today. Everyone would then become eager adherents of Cai Bau. A Philippine-American biology professor, a kind of mixture between Jeanne d'Arc and Buddha, who could lecture for five hours without a script, but who made it seem like only ten minutes, was planning to lead the new world order that was just around the corner. When your father wasn't expounding on alternative religions, the largest part of his life was spent on matters regarding sausage. The first time I visited you, he came into your bedroom and sat down on the sofa. He yanked out the Nintendo cable and told us to listen. This was the first of the sausage stories we heard from his repertoire. A few years earlier, he had been on a business trip in the town of Bø in Telemark to meet with the municipality about erecting Norway's first Cai Bau temple. As usual, his stomach had to be filled with a sausage in order for him to sleep. His sharp eyes scrutinized the menu of the local hotdog stand, noting the typical Norwegian fast food specialities *beef-pops, leafy-beefies* and *hawaii burgers*. He gave a satisfactory nod of recognition upon seeing onion hotdogs appear on the not-so-shabby list of victuals offered at Bø's fast food kitchen. But he nearly lost his breath when he noticed small writing at the bottom of the menu: "Luxury sausage 85 dollars." Instead of considering whether the hotdog stand owner was an exploitative hog of a man, he slammed down a handful of bills on the countertop. The two minutes it took for the sausage to be prepared were almost unbearable. He trembled with joy in anticipation of this new sausage experience, and a Norwegian one to boot. What audacity, what a collective raising of the bar among Norway's sausage culture! His eyes keenly tracked each minute movement. The man in the window walked into the back room and brought out a small tin can from the fridge. He then removed a Leiv Vidar sausage, and your father nodded approvingly, because Leiv Vidar was one of the few sausage makers in Norway that he found acceptable, even if they had become quite commercial and adapted their brand to the market in recent years. He leaned over the bar and stuck his hand liberally into the water where the cook stood, to check that it was the proper temperature. He licked his fingers, to be sure that the water hadn't been standing since the morning. Everything was more than satisfactory, and his expectation increased. Then the man in the window lay the sausage in a bed of perfectly heated bread, opened the tin, stuck a plastic knife into it and spread 25 grams of Russian caviar across the sausage. Your father took two bites of the

sausage before resolutely wiping off the caviar with his index finger, flicking it onto the ground, and eating the rest
of the sausage plain. He was indignant that anyone could
thus ruin a perfectly good sausage. Gustimoldo. In retrospect, I believe there are two things that can push people over the edge and into an endless plummet: time and
money. Since both of your parents went on welfare permanently, without any obligations each morning they had all
the time in the world to realize the worst in themselves.
The tipping point was when your father inherited the villa
in Fredrikstad and gained millions. There is nothing that
makes a slightly crazy person go completely bonkers then
when they achieve financial freedom. Your parents were
idiots in the true sense of the word. They were outliers, far
on the outskirts of society.

Do you remember that time your father woke us up in the
middle of the night, told us to put on our slippers and come
into the kitchen? His mood was easy, but we could sense
that something was coming. He put his finger to his mouth
to signal that we must keep very quiet so as not to wake
your mother, and then he pulled out the old sausage making apparatus that was packed away behind the casserole
dishes in the lowest cabinet. Wearing old working clothes,
he brought out the mill and a roll of sausage casings on a
sheet of plastic. While frying up the noisettes earlier that
day, he had also secretly been preparing the garlic, capers,
sage, thyme, chives, and ginger that were now laid out in
prep dishes along the kitchen counter. In the refrigerator,
sandwiched between the nail polish and tray of perfume
were some very fine cuts of pork neck and ram. Then he
put on the album that meant the most to him in the world,
"Mr. Hands" by Herbie Hancock, and began grinding
for dear life, with you and I as horrified onlookers. In the

midst of this emotionally challenging context, of spending quality time with his son and the sausage-high, the tales of ridicule and soap-box sermons flowed unabridged. Your father told us about how he, as a young sausage maker, had been sent by the National Pork Association to west Berlin in 1961. He spoke in reverent tones about his encounter with Kaufhaus des Westens on Kurfürstendamm:

> *At our butcher shops back home, there were only two types of sausage you could get in those days, smoked and unsmoked, and if you were real lucky, blood sausage. Can you understand my joy, then, when I came to KaDeWe and witnessed 847 different varieties swimming before my eyes? I stepped up to the deli counter, which measured a whole 39.5 metres. There were heaps of sausages, with different seasonings, variations in grind, in layout, in casings and with new methods for hanging them. A world of possibilities! Veal sausage with allspice from Naples, malted beer sausage from Holland, venison and sage blood sausage from Basel, lamb breakfast sausage with thyme from Milan and Berlin's own classic currywurst. But it didn't stop there. Sheep sausage infused with truffle oil and thick sausages of wild boar from the Black Forest, where even the fat contained its own unique flavour. The skin smelled so good that a muskox could faint from it. As you know, boys, a sausage is never just a sausage, it is a country's history, its cultural backbone, the manifestation of its spirit—the deliverance unto a richer world.*

From where he stood imitating Hancock's arp-synthesizer on "Just Around the Corner" with a half-stuffed sausage in his hand, it was clear that your father's experience at KaDeWe in 1961 had made it impossible for him ever to return to the tiny butcher shop in Fredrikstad where he had worked as an apprentice. When he returned from his study tour, he used his inheritance from an aunt, supplemented by loans from the Fredrikstad Bank, to purchase the ultimate, most state-of-the-art sausage-making equipment that money could buy, from a factory on the outskirts of Genoa. A few months later, he officially opened Northern Europe's most exclusive sausage boutique, "La Maison de Gourmet de Saucisse" in the Fredrikstad market square, complete with an attending, dazed French cultural attaché from the embassy. At this point in his sermon, your father was convinced that he was hot on the pathway of truth.

> *Even though my vision for a specialized butcher shop for sausages in eastern Norway had been realized, there were harder times ahead. Because Norwegians' tastes were much less cultivated than the rest of Europe's. Sales of the typical sausages were tremendous, but I was forced to donate large amounts of my 27 gourmet sausage varieties to the Salvation Army. And even there, people politely refused to touch the sausages. You understand, boys, Norway wasn't like it is now. People were afraid in those days. Those new sausages were seen as a threat to traditional lamb stew and meatballs and became a symbol of the growing elitism in the Norwegian society. A wise man once said that it is in good times that one must erect new structures for the future, but it isn't right for pioneers to do so—they create out of nothing. The work that pioneers such as me did in those times has laid the groundwork for the*

*type of sausage makers who didn't use to exist in
our country. Our tireless struggle has finally paid
off in a fully developed sausage culture. I have
friends in Scotland and Belgium who, when they
come to visit Norway, the first thing that they do
when they land at Gardermoen airport is to run
off in search of grilled sausages at Narvesen. That
tells you something.*

Depressed and bankrupt, he was finally forced to shut
down his boutique after several months. Rather than admit defeat, he locked himself in his parent's cellar for two
months. One could hear sounds of whisks and squeaking
machinery, and couriers often came by with deliveries.
Then one autumn day, he finally emerged from the cellar.
"This is not a comeback," he told the local newspaper in
an article with the headline: "Finally, something has happened in eastern Norway!" In the same interview, he invited all of Fredrikstad to the launch of his newest prod-
uct which, according to him, "would bring together high
and low culture in a synchronized unity never before
witnessed in intellectual history." In a grand spectacle,
which must have been one of the saddest sights that the
universe has ever seen, he had, in the night's dark hours,
rigged together an eight metre high scaffolding on wheels
in the Fredrikstad market square. With the use of a meg-
aphone, he sat perched atop the pulpit broadcasting his
ideas about sausages to the Saturday shoppers whilst his
loyal parents handed out samples and wheeled the scaf-
fold around town. The police showed up with several patrols but kept their distance because they feared that the
homemade tower of babel might come crashing down atop
of the crowds. From his provocative position, your father
unveiled his latest invention, the "E6-sausage." Just as his

beloved Cai Bau religion attempted to bring together all of the world's religions, the E6-sausage followed the same principle. The sausage represented all of the Norwegian people, from the south to the north, its sweeping terrain, myriad of species, indigenous peoples, immigrants, bedrock, flora, lakes and soul. The sausage filling originated primarily from animals that had become roadkill along the E6 north-south motorway. Your father had entered into a revolutionary agreement with the Roadway Administration and Game Committee that allowed him to collect an assortment of killed animals. So the list of ingredients included moose, deer, badgers, foxes and cats. The spices in the sausage also originated from different regions along the E6. Dried moss from Gudbrandsdal and kale from Lofoten. In addition to a business concept that was economically grounded in the readily available natural resources, he also had a plan to distribute the sausage at gas stations along the E6 route. This distribution network, built from a grassroots level or based on a pyramid scheme if one wished, would make the E6-sausage one of the most popular national products. Your father was wheeled around by his parents through the streets of Fredrikstad until late in the evening, hammering his megaphoned message home to the town's inhabitants. There's no doubt that the E6-sausage was very tasty. But for the average person, who he was trying to reach out to, it was too special. When the sun set and your father refused to stop his announcements, the police collected him with a crane and booked him into an institution. It was here that he met your mother, who hated sausage, but loved noisettes. This is why it was especially important that your mother shouldn't find out about our nocturnal activities. On this evening, we sat up until the early hours, eating kilo after kilo of gourmet sausages to remove all traces. When our stomachs bulged and we had finally finished washing all the equipment, it was time to stick our fingers in his open wounds. Gustimoldo, you couldn't help yourself. You began by provocatively mentioning photos of Haile Selassie I from Ethiopia, in which he is serving pork chops to his dogs. "I told you, Gustimoldo, those pictures were fabricated by the CIA!" he screamed, tearing at small tufts of hair on his head. Or, well, I should correct myself. Your father barely had any hair left on his head. He had two thick dreads of hair near his ears, which he twisted together at the top of his head. He would tear even harder at the dreads when you started arguing that the Incas—his lifelong heroes—were really despots who sacrificed children, and that they would never wear their hand-sewn clothes more than once. They were "poppin tags" long before the age of mass production and Jay-Z, that's how over-the-top affluent they had been. This pushed your father over the edge, thus achieving your goal. You could take punch after punch after that, it didn't matter to you, this was all a part of your childhood routine. It was a hundred times more rewarding for you to get him to show his real face. Your father pushed the sausage stuffing down in the casing between two fingers so that it became a sledgehammer. And then he was off after you, swinging at you while you ran, hopped, ducked, turned and screamed at him: "Sausage narcissist! Sausage narcissist!" You stood singing out the words on top of the kitchen table, and he met you with a well-placed blow on your face. You immediately collapsed and fell lifelessly to the floor. He walked slowly over to you and began beating you countless times until the sausage casing broke and guts and ground pork with sage burst over your bloody face. In situations such as this, after he had completely lost his reason, your father would lock himself inside the laundry room. Here he would conduct a bit of self-therapy with action painting to get out his bad feelings. Throughout the night, we boys heard continuous guttural sounds. This signalled that he had switched over to slam poetry to release the rest of his aggression. At other times, he would turn up Don Cherry's "Organic Music Society" to full volume and hum along. We cowered under the bed, the two of us, clinging to each other and crying amidst the unrelenting stench of sausage that refused to dissipate. Gustimoldo, I don't think the beating was the worst thing. I believe that what was most painful was your father's inconsistency. If he had come down from the loft and declared that his new name was "Scorpion" and that he now belonged to an ancient Australian religion, you were required to suck it up and deal with it.

To accept it.

You always answered my questions by saying: "Should I be honest or humanistic?" I try to write as honestly as I can, and I hope that my letters attest to this. You and I draw closer each moment, we tear off one another's masks and sit beneath the sun as the stick figures that we truly are. Gustimoldo, you alone should judge yourself—you are entitled to this.

And then come home.

Dear Gustimoldo

I couldn't sleep tonight. Stomach pains. I thought it might be acid reflux, so I drank several litres of water to balance it all out. The rest of the night was spent pissing.

I removed all of the curtains in the house and turned on all the lamps.

Can you see me now—can you see that I want to finish our task?

DAG SOLSTAD'S TAXI RECEIPT (1996)

Originating from the time that Grandma and Solstad travelled down the Rhine valley during their autumn vacation. He was responsible for remembering the name of their hotel before they left for the disco. He rushed reluctantly into the lobby, memorised the name on the sign, and came out again. In the taxi on the way home late that night, Solstad suddenly screamed out, "To Hotel Ausgang, please!" Grandma was furious when she realised Solstad's blunder.

Paper
VG
JG1112

LUCHINO VISCONTIS' BEER MAT (1971)

From the evening that Grandma and Visconti took the actor Björn Andrésen to a gay bar during the filming of *Death in Venice*. On the back, Visconti wrote to Grandma: "I am Aschenbach. Be my Tadzio. Coochy coo."

Cardboard
G (beer stains)
JG1113

LEO TROTSKY AND OLAV ANDREAS SCHEFLO'S WARM APPLES (1935)

Fallen apples dipped in pancake batter and baked on a bonfire pan. Originates from the time Trotsky and his wife Natalia Sedova lived in exile at Sundby in Hurum while fleeing from Stalin in 1935. Between struggling to finish his book, *The Revolution Betrayed,* and arguing with the Norwegian Minister of Justice, Trygve Lie, Trotsky, Scheflo and Grandma found time to enjoy the calm summer days and their small joys.

Apples
G (rotted and half eaten)
JG1114

BUSHWICK BILL'S BLOODY EYEPATCH (1993)

The bloody eyepatch originates from when Grandma, Scarface and Willie D went to visit Bill at the hospital after his attempted suicide. Though the bullet went in through the eye, he miraculously survived. Grandma was terribly sorry that she and Willie had poured so much Everclear in Bill's glass that evening, which had made him a bit more wildly emotional than usual.

Gauze with dried blood
G+
JG1115

CHARLIE CHAPLIN'S WAFFLE IRON (1940)

Very heavy waffle iron that Grandma stole from the set of *The Great Dictator,* where she had been hired as stylist for her good friend Paulette Goddard.

Metal, electrical cord
G+ (covered in solidified waffle batter)
JG1116

NECKLACE FROM FRANK ZAPPA (1973)

Grandma received this necklace the night after the concert on Kalvøya Island in 1973. The inscription on the backside reads: "You've just been fucked by Frank Zappa." Also on the back in scrawny letters, most likely scratched in with a sewing needle, it says: "And George Duke too."

Fake gold
VG
JG1117

FERNANDO ARRABAL'S BATHROBE (1991)

A gift from Fernando for Grandma during their sword fishing tour on Hawaii in 1991. The trip came about after she decided to take him away from Paris following his breakdown at the showing of Jodorowsky's film *Santa Sangre*. A note in the bathrobe pocket reads: "I am ashamed to belong to the Panic-Movement ensuing from this shit-film. His sons—good god! We ended up worse than Dollar-Dalí."

Bathrobe with a paper note
VG-
JG1118

HARRY PARTCH'S HANDKERCHIEF (1951)
Used during the recording of *Eleven Intrusions* when Partch came down with a bad cold. The handkerchief was later given to Grandma as a token of love from Tom Waits, who had acquired it at an auction in London, in appreciation of an enchanting evening together in Queens in 1978.

Cotton
NM
JG1119

CYPRIEN GAILLARD'S AIRPLANE TICKET STUB (2010)
Used when Gaillard travelled to Iraq in 2010 to create the piece *Babylon*. Grandma and Cyprien were on the same flight from Paris to Baghdad and got to know each other during a stopover in Turkey. She served as Gaillard's interpreter and lover during the entire tour, and stole the ticket stub when he went to visit the cultural attaché at the French Consulate located in the green zone.

Glossy paper
VG
JG11120

APICHATPONG WEERASETHAKUL'S HORSERADISH HAND CREAM (2004)
Homemade cream that Grandma received on the set of *Sud*

sanaeha in gratitude for her assistance to Weerasethakul in casting her old friend, Jenjira Jansuda, in one of the main roles.

Horseradish, wasabi, pepper, yoghurt, galingale root
G- (mould on the upper edge)
JG1121

MEREDITH MONK'S DOORMAT (1991)
Stolen by Grandma after a tutoring appointment at Meredith Monk's place in New York, where she went to study ululation, multiphonics and vocal vibrato. Written on the mat are the words "Be gentle. Keep Trying."

Straw and strands of linen
NM
JG1122

ULISES CARRIÓN'S HORN RIMMED GLASSES WITH PAPER (1973)
Glass frames and paper originating from Carrión's performance piece "Book". On the inside of the paper is a dedication to Grandma, which reads: "In the old art, the writer wrote texts / In the new art, the writer writes books. Kisses, Ulises."

A4-page and Ray Ban glasses
VG- (crumpled page and surface scratches on lenses)
JG1123

DZIGA VERTOV'S CINEMA TICKET (1929)
Originating from the premiere of Dziga Vertov's Cinema Glaz manifesto from 1922 at the Moscow Cinema. On the back of the ticket, Dziga wrote that he, Mikhail, Boris and all of Cinema Pravda were infinitely appreciative of her presence during the filming of *The Man With the Film Camera*. He writes that old Eisenstein spoke about the film as: "A relic from the age of steel and wheels," but as long as Grandma

was there with her loud whoop, he couldn't have been more satisfied. "Kisses from a distant land, Dziga."

Paper
VG-
JG1124

KARLHEINZ STOCKHAUSEN'S FOUR TRACK MASTER TAPES OF GESANG DER JÜNGLINGE (1955)

AGFA one inch tape containing several unused vocal tracks with Josef Protschka on *Gesang der Jünglinge,* recorded in the WDR radio studio in Cologne. Stockhausen writes that he is full of anticipation waiting for a response from Herbert Eimert's letter to the bishop in Cologne where he has asked whether the mass might be performed in the cathedral, even if he doesn't really expect anything wonderful to happen.

Tape
VG- (tape was stored in unsuitable storage facilities for 40 years. Whacky tape, needs to be baked)
JG1125

U-J3RK5 CONCERT POSTER FROM OR GALLERY (1980)

Concert poster for Rodney Graham, Jeff Wall and Ian Wallace's band, U-J3RK5. The poster was designed by Dan Graham as a gesture after the band's song "Eisenhower and the Hippies" was dedicated to him. Grandma pulled the poster from a lamppost in Vancouver on her way to the after party at Jeff Wall's place.

Paper
VG- (tear in lower left corner)
JG1126

WIFREDO LAM'S HUMIDOR (1964)

Acquired on Grandma's trip to Havana to help the Cuban government in their negotiations for higher sugar prices from the Soviet Union and GDR. During her travels, she stayed in Wifredo's guest room, and when he left for his studio early in the morning, Grandma took his humidor and fled to the airport.

Oak
VG (some discolouration in the finish and worn out corners)
JG1127

JENS BJØRNEBOE'S PROPELLER (1975)

From the time that Bjørneboe and Grandma held a midsummer's eve party on Veierland and annoyed the hell out of all the neighbours within a mile's circumference. Drunk to the brim, Bjørneboe started up his yacht and hit land when he ran aground in a small bay. Early the next morning, Grandma took her morning swim near the site of the accident. She dove underwater for over a minute's time and appeared again on the surface with a propeller between her teeth.

Metal
VG-
JG1128

Dear Gustimoldo

Days without a rind.

You used this expression to describe our time together. Did you mean the days when flesh overran its rind and no barrier could hold it back? The days that we spent dangling helplessly on a rubber band, stretched taut between our unforgivable human thoughts of superiority and our isolated self-hatred?

Days without rind, in which one sprints back and forth at a breathless pace, never managing to locate oneself between those weightless, peaceful moments. One day I find myself sitting at Hansen's bakery, eating napoleon cakes and thinking napoleon thoughts. Some hours later there's nothing left but a sense of guilt and failure, an inevitable dissolution of one's own self worth. When the rubber band tends in this direction, my self-image is so low that I imagine myself existing only as sweat among the bed sheets.

It is at these moments that I am no longer in possession of myself, Gustimoldo.

You cannot degrade someone who is unable to judge himself. Even worse, you cannot love a person who is unable to judge himself. So we continue, Gustimoldo, tethered to this lifelong bungee cord, catapulted outward by the force of misunderstood lives, bouncing up and down with the smile of children on our faces.

We lived days without a rind.

You always said that my greatest challenge was being unable to accept the privileged situation into which I was born. In one of your scientific magazines, you read that the chance of being born into such prosperity as mine was as likely as throwing a dice 36 times and having it land on six every time. 36 throws of the dice, and this was the prize? You wanted to celebrate the historical slump that our generation was born into. "Isn't this what our forefathers fought for?" you asked rhetorically, implying that we could afford to crack a tiny smile, since we had now reached the top of the food chain.

May you have no pain but champagne!

Would not everything else have been sheer madness?

Sometimes I imagined a lonesome figure, leaning solitarily over a table in a casino where the oxygen sat heavy like a layer of fog above the tables, the green felt breathing. After having rolled sixes ten times in a row, our figure's skin begins to crawl with an irritated, sneaking suspicion every time he casts the dice. He thinks that perhaps there is some trick, some hidden camera, and so he checks the dice and rattles his hand differently for each cast. His hand is in a new position when he lets the dice roll. Sixes again. He continues to cast, and the dice continues to reveal only sixes. His tension lessens. Happiness takes the upper hand, why not? He dances wildly atop the casino table. The dice thrower is alone in the room. He begins to think about his winnings and what he will do with them. But later. He hurls the dice violently against the table to try and knock one of the eyes off, but no one notices as it lands on sixes on the floor. A muted anxiety edges its way into his intense delight and pride. Just as in every other casino, one cannot tell the time of day from inside the room. Pure oxygen pours from metal pipes fastened to the wall so that they resemble a church organ. It is impossible to find an exit. Sixes. He has thrown the dice 23 times and rolled sixes every time. He feels invincible. His luck cannot change as long as he still desires it. Onlookers have started gathering to honour the new master and his courage. A new idea surfaces, one that is not easy to shake: the fear of the 37th throw. He knows that this fateful moment will come, when there will no longer be six black eyes staring up at him. He's forgotten the extraordinary circumstances, that he has thrown sixes 25 times in a row. The 37th throw is coming. Only 12 more throws, and he has lost his count. It is at this moment that he remembers the odds and decides to bet that there won't be any 37th throw. His strategy is to refuse to play. He wants out, he needs to talk with someone in charge. He has to get out of this casino, now. It feels as though he has been there for decades, though he only arrived forty minutes ago. But he must throw, there is no way out, and he lets the dice fall from his hand one last time on the table. It rolls and stops at a six.

Is this what I cannot accept, Gustimoldo?

As you have most likely guessed by now, the rubber band is stretched in the wrong direction today. No sign of life from you and I am alone in the house. On the one side, piles of jutegnask, and on the other, the pull of our research. The black histories are crying out to be made into signs. Gustimoldo—my life is in the month of March. The month where people can only hope that seeds exists, that roots exist, that the sticks hanging from the trees are indeed branches. The summer is over. The autumn is over. Winter too. The only thing for people to do in the month of March is to hope that all of this indefinable, silent brown machinery will once again start working. That the awakening of spring will somehow reoccur. If you were here now, you would tousle my hair and say, gently:

> *Do you remember what the lazy old bum told the idealist as he crossed the threshold to save the world?*

> *It's never too late to become a dirty old man.*

I know, Gustimoldo, but can I save that trump card to the end? I am so tired of waiting and writing these letters to you. It requires more of my strength than even the jutegnask and the black signs. Without you, I am just a computer character on the final level. The life-barometer is measuring in at alarmingly low levels. I'm blinking and need to see half a heart or a star to continue. I am, as always, headed towards the Final Boss.

Dear Gustimoldo

I wake up in the morning knowing that my dreams in the night have been of the day that is beginning. The day becomes a repetition of the dream that has foretold its events down to every last detail. In the dream, I am cataloguing jutegnask items, packaging them in cardboard boxes and shipping them out in the delivery trucks. After digesting my lunch, I begin on orders for black signs until sleep takes me. I awake and relive the dream again in a waking state.

Come home, Gustimoldo.
Come forth, Gustimoldo.

Dear Gustimoldo

Roots cast no shadows.

The cold, sharp autumn has arrived in Oslo, it gleams in the garden. While taking a break between the working hours, I wrapped myself in a blanket and tried to nap with the TV playing in the background. It was early in the afternoon and the programme replayed old newsreels from the fifties. A close-up sign illuminated the screen, it said "Community Centre." The next image is of a group of young people, all with Down syndrome, sitting around a table covered with coca cola and cake. As the camera turns toward them, they laugh and fool around, they realize they are being captured on film. The boys wear suits, button down shirts, bow or neckties. The whole thing is orchestrated. The girls are in long dresses and jewellery. Also orchestrated. Bobby pins hold their hairstyles in place, while the boys most likely had to an apply hair wax and wear a cap the night before. The TV-announcer says: "These young people seem to be having a grand time at the dance gala put on by the Oslo Society of Housemothers and The Helpers of Weak Souls. They are enjoying soda and home-made baked goods while swinging in tune to the evening rhythms." The scene shifts to the parents outside, sitting in their cars and waiting to pick up their children. Some smoke out the windows, some smile as they are spotted by the cameras, some sit stiffly. Others try to hide their faces with their hands. "Many of the parents have allowed their children to enjoy the time inside alone while they wait patiently in their cars outside." Shift to a new scene. The youth dance with their arms around one another's waists. There is some pinching and gentle caresses here and there. They hold on tightly to each other, arms locked behind backs. A trio stands in the background, playing rockabilly. The band members also have Down syndrome and tall, slicked-back hairstyles. The TV emits a flat, monotonous bass from one of the amplifiers, accompanied by some light brushes on the drums. Towering above the microphone, the vocalist grabs hold of the stand with his right hand, leans over and sings something that might be reminiscent of a limp version of "Love Me Tender." It is a fearless interpretation of the Elvis classic, in which one can only barely discern the words, rhythms and harmonies. Then, out of the blue, the voice says: "What is interesting is that mentally retarded people don't have natural sexual drives like normal people. When they choose a partner, dance and cry, it is only out of a desire to resemble us. They are merely copycats."

Where did that come from?

The scene shifts. In sync, the parents enter the hall to collect their children and the party breaks up. Some individuals, hoping for one last dance, begin to cry as they realize that the band has left the stage. The cars drive away from the community centre parking lot one after another.

> *And now they are off home to go to sleep and start the countdown for the 364 days until the next party.*

I believe you and I are copycats, Gustimoldo. We don't have the same drive as others do. They tried to stuff us full of knowledge and manners from day one, but it was as though we were immune, it all went in one ear and out the other. We would pretend to understand, and cram before each exam. But the next day we would forget everything again, like it had been swept from our memories. Can you recall their excitement when they saw how their knowledge was passed on? If only they had known that our education, our being and very marrow was based on the deliberate forgetfulness and misunderstanding of their teachings. We raised our defence against any imposed information. We deconstructed ourselves to build ourselves up. So we thought. Creating our own backbone. The task was slightly more extensive than we thought. As I write this letter to you, Gustimoldo, I can't help for some reason think of the Pink Panther films, with Peter Sellers in the leading role, which we used to watch together. In the films, Inspector Clouseau instructed the Chinese kung fu expert, Cato Fong, to attack him without warning at any time. His knowledge that Cato was out there, ready to pounce, helped him to remain alert at all times and to take necessary precautions. Just like Clouseau, we erected our own Fong, always prepared to counter-attack their onslaught.

Their roots cast no shadows into our souls.

There is little that I remember from my childhood, Gustimoldo. No songs, no playgrounds or birthday parties. There are other snippets of memory, however, that have remained with me. Such as the day we read that, for the first time in the company's history, McDonald's had incurred a deficit. We both burst into spontaneous tears. We were ten at the time, and felt an overwhelming pang of sorrow that this company—which had been so generous and friendly to us in our childhoods, with straws and ketchup and napkins—should now have fallen on difficult times. We dreamt at night of genetic mutations, systemic crashes, and watched the moon collapse outside our window. As teenagers, we spent our free time not at recreation clubs and libraries, but rather at sprawling shopping malls, subterranean parking garages and poorly guarded construction sites. Among sales tags, cement machines, ATMs and tectyl spray, we found everything that meant anything to us, anything that could provide a sense of meaning. We scattered nail cartridges along the tracks and danced in jubilation when the streetcar drove over them. We filled up 0.33 litre cola bottles with gas and said it was for our toy cars. The attendants at the petrol stations didn't bother worrying. Then we doused the neighbourhood's intercoms in gasoline and lit them ablaze. We watched as the plastic slowly melted in the flames and heard the cacophony of voices wondering in unison who might be calling now.

Although we had no faith, we went to confirmation; everyone wanted a little piece of God, and we wanted cash. Our days led to petty crimes, perfecting the art of lying, and competing at deflowering virgins. The incineration chimney at Ullevål hospital belched out the remains of our aborted foetuses, and when it rained, distributed them across Oslo. Gustimoldo—we were guilty, but whenever the gavel fell, we were always deemed minors. Our supreme court was our restless, immediate gratification. We were never turned in for any of our crimes. At the age of 14, we stood outside the polling stations handing out blank ballot sheets we had drawn up and copied ourselves. On the other side of the doors stood representatives for the Labour and Conservative parties. The older gentlemen told us that they had once been like us, full of youthful engagement and enthusiasm. "That's as it should be. But one day you will be on the same side as us."

They were the very epitome of depravity.

In the meanwhile, the societal wheel cranked forward,

unaffected by our lack of development. That is to say, the jobs, positions and opinions of our parent's generation were passed down to us. Our generation became crippled by that secret of conformity that does not allow for imitation without some measure of exaggeration. We became like our parents, only worse, if possible. Everything that took place around us was akin to when the petrol station owner handed his key to his son with the mandate: "Now it's up to you to carry the torch." All those Brady Bunch kids from hell that we knew from school suddenly became doctors, academics, judges, agents, journalists, economists and disappeared. We stood on the sidelines and refused to join in.

We were December children in the truest sense.

The day I turned 20, Gustimoldo, I was a friendless stump. I watched a television quiz show where adults competed against six-year olds and realized that I would have been a resounding loser in such a competition. I was incapable. I almost couldn't write, that's how far we had succeeded in deconstructing ourselves. The only greeting I received for my birthday was an SMS from the Bislet Car Rental service and a congratulatory email from Amazon.com with several rebate offers. Fortunately, you turned up on my doorstep, proud as a peacock. You presented me with the black book as a gift and said, "I think you will like this." Yes, Gustimoldo, it was the best gift I have ever received. Inside the book was a birthday card containing some lines of Keats:

> *Beauty is truth, truth beauty, — that is all*
> *Ye know on earth, and all ye need to know.*

Gustimoldo, you are such a riot.

Dear Gustimoldo

A brief question.

Do you recall anything about the remains of a mallard in the attic—was it a prank that we pulled or a relic from some performance?

A swift reply is required.

Dear Gustimoldo

The black book. The name stirs up feelings of respect and disgust within me. As if it would bring curses upon me to speak its name.

The black book was the Church City Mission's protocol log documenting events which occurred among the city's marginalized populations, drug addicts and prostitutes. If anything happened to any of the clients of the City Mission, the victim was instructed to head down to an office in the Grønland neighbourhood of Oslo where a social worker would patiently record every last detail of the event. Since in this context, violence or abuse were almost never reported to the police, the protocol formed an alternative historical account next to the official version. The first thing that really captivated us about the black book was its dual function—it brought a previously unknown story to light while simultaneously functioning as an alternative system to prevent further abuses. The black book both documented and prevented, but it was something even more which it is difficult to find words for. In its basic and fundamental elements, it had the ability to significantly raise peoples' awareness. Our particular copy of the black book spanned a time period of a mere six months. Yet it was bursting at the seams and contained hundreds of pages. In it were dates, locations, and descriptions of rape, robbery and abuse, each sordid event recorded in detail. I read it cover to cover in the first sitting. One prostitute had her teeth pulled out with a sophisticated meat clip because her customer accused her of trying to contact his wife after their last meeting. Another character, who was often mentioned, was a man from Sri Lanka that several of the women described as shorter than 140 cm. He offered each of the women 1000 dollars to have sex with his German shepherd, which always sat with its tongue out on the back seat of his station wagon. Most of them refused and added, "that they would never go along with such a thing, one has to have limits." Security guards and shop owners from the city's many shopping centres are frequent guests among the pages. Meticulous descriptions detailed how they would bring drug addicts whom they suspected of theft down into a hidden room which they rented in an underground parking lot below the shopping centre. Here, they doused the addicts with water and released them into the Oslo winter. And in the summer, when this routine for natural reasons was ineffective, they would beat them flat with plastic bags over their hands. The detail that the security guards forced their victims to clean up their own blood after their beatings really got to me, Gustimoldo. One girl was held captive in an apartment by five men who raped her repeatedly and threatened her with a drug overdose if she said anything. She claims to have been held in the apartment for at least a month, perhaps two or four, and claimed to have lived off of biscuits and canned food that she found in the kitchen. One of the men put his mobile phone in her vagina and dialled the number. She sat splayed and ringing to the group's delight. She chose not to prosecute, she couldn't remember things so well. The whole thing was filmed and she was afraid to report the situation in case the clip would be publicized online. There are often additional notes from one of the Church City Mission's employees in the protocol, such as: "The man who X describes has often come to the door of the City Mission and acted aggressively." A former priest and member of the Oslo Church Council, who always used to brag to the girls that he was a close friend of Jens Bjørneboe in the early 1970s, as if that fact was supposed to provide credibility, reportedly offered large sums of money to male drug addicts to be able to spend time alone with their children. He only wanted to hug them, he said. One client overheard the priest saying to his child: "May I suckle on your wee wee?" and ran in to put a stop to the whole thing. That was apparently too much, even for him. A professor of musicology who lived alone in a large villa in Røa was often mentioned in the book. Although the very essence of gentility during the negotiations about money and location, the scene would always end with him beating the crap out of the prostitutes and accusing them of intended burglary. As he hit them, he would scream something to the effect of: "It's people like you who burgle, slink around, tag and ruin our society!" I have decided that the black book's greatest quality is that it hovers somewhere between intoxicating fantasy and incomprehensible reality. It refuses to land. Most often, it is as sobering as a winter day in Norway, but it twinkles with some of the most manneristic fearful fantasies that I have ever read. It's like attending the funeral of a young, dead friend and watching the casket being lowered into the grave where icicles have formed along the edges of the earth—the black book endows you with a great desire to live, it is a perpetual *momento mori*.

Our idea was as simple as it was good. We would use the black book as a template for a project to write an alternative, revised history: the black history. It wasn't only the black book's ability to raise awareness and document that appealed to us. We understood that the task of writing the black history, of peering deeply into this indefinable, dark quagmire and bringing it to light so that each and every inhabitant in Oslo could participate, was the perfect subversive strategy for undermining their fixed modes of perception. This would not merely induce a passive catharsis, as in art, but rather it would be provide a way to personally participate in the catharsis. By digging up each person's individual black history, one would be able to discuss the actions of every person on an individual basis, and not with large swaths of generalizations that the official historical accounts tended to focus on. We would be able, for the first time, to have a historical account and view of reality that included all of humanity. Gustimoldo, don't you remember? We began to compile our research archive, based on the black histories, on all that was unofficial, non-existent, reversed. We founded the Black Cultural Historical Institute and researched everything that society tried to avoid. We hoped to spread the black history by carpet bombing the entire country with tens of thousands of black signs, our corrective solution to the official blue signs describing cultural heritage sites.

A form of revenge.

They had it coming.

WALT DISNEY'S CURLING IRON (1946)

This pre-historical and extremely dangerous curling iron was a gift given in appreciation to Grandma for mitigating a burgeoning conflict between Walt and Salvador Dalí. The argument arose in 1946 after the former decided to shelve Dalí's cartoon Destino because of economic difficulties in the aftermath of World War II.

Plastic and metal
VG+ (unused, still in original cardboard packaging)
JG24201

POSTAL CORRESPONDENCE BETWEEN GRANDMA AND FOROUGH FARROKHZÂD (1962)

On yellowed newsprint from the Iranian newspaper Donya-e-Eqtesads, the morning edition from February 12, 1962, is an exhaustive correspondence between Grandma and Farrokhzâd. In which they specifically discuss an informational film about leprosy in Northern Iran which she hopes to start filming as soon as possible.

Paper
G- (water damage to the paper makes the text unreadable at times)
JG24202

GIORGIO MORANDIS' WINDOWSILL FLY (1938)

While waiting for Morandi to return home from his daytime job at the Accademia di Belle Arti di Bologna, Grandma took the opportunity to collect a few small mementos from the flat. A painted bottle, a sport totebag containing a wet towel and white tennis shoes, and this dead fly that had perished on a windowsill.

Fly
G- (only two legs and one wing remaining)
JG24203

SIGRID UNDSET'S TURNSTILE (1934)

The wooden gate at the entrance of the stone cabin at Lyng-kampen, where Grandma and Undset spent many summers together. On the accompanying note, Grandma complains that Sigrid insists on replacing the sod roof every single summer, which in her view is a result of Undset's misguided masculinity. While Undset worked on the roof, Grandma pulled the turnstile from the ground, dismantled it piece by piece, and packed it into a backpack.

Wood and iron
VG-
JG24204

LAJOS KASSÁK'S SHOPSKA SALAD (1934)

Biological leftovers of a salad leaf, goat cheese and onions together in a plastic bag. From a Serbian shopska salad enjoyed at a sidewalk restaurant in Novi Sad in the summer of 1925. Grandma had called a meeting with the editors of the magazines UT, Zenit, MAVO, Secession, DAV, Pasmo, Der Sturm and De Stijl to have, as the main agenda item, a discussion on "a common platform for European distribution."

Organic bits in a plastic bag
G-
JG24205

ПЕРЕД СНЕГОМ BY ARSENIJ TARKOVSKIJ (1983)

A signed copy of the poetry collection Перед снегом (After the Snowfall), given to Grandma by Andrej Tarkovskij following the shooting of the film Nostalghia in Italy. The inscription reads: "Vadim and I are so sincerely grateful that you distracted Erland Josephson throughout the night and into the next day. You are such an angel."

Bound book
VG+
JG24206

LETTER FROM ROBERT CRUMB (1977)

Written on a piece of stationary: "I miss the enormous, bulging, muscular trunks of your legs and hips. I hope you have continued your daily hikes to keep those two tightly rounded buns in shape. A note from my liver: I am wild for your burrito sauce, which is much more tasteful than Honey Bunch Kaminski's insipid attempts to play to the gallery, can you spare a few bottles per post?"

Paper
VG+
JG24207

JAN KJÆRSTAD'S COPY OF THE LANDSTAD REVISED HYMNAL (1975)

Originating from the time that Kjærstad played as the rhythmic guitarist in the Ten Sing choir Impuls and in the Christian jazz rock group Færder Fyr. Grandma pinched this from backstage at the Jesus Festival in Molde in 1975. On the back, Kjærstad has written: "Show us the way" and "Olaf Hillestad rules!"

Pages in a binder
G+/VG
JG24208

INVITATION TO A LAURIE ANDERSON EXHIBIT AT STEDELIJK (1982)

A handwritten invitation from Laurie Anderson to Grandma regarding the exhibition "60/80, Attitudes/Concepts/Images" at the Stedelijk Museum in Amsterdam. She writes that she sends many greetings from Jana Haimsohn in New York, and also that she finds it outstanding that Grandma's LP copy of Jules Massenet's opera has led to so much fuss in the last years.

Paper card
VG- (soda stains on the invitation)
JG24209

POSTCARD FROM PABLO NERUDA (1949)

The image on the postcard is the summer palace in Beijing. Neruda writes that he has become consulate in China for Chile, almost against his will. He misses the sea air and the sound of cargo ships. He is comforted, however, in that he will finally be able to travel to Lhasa, which has been a long-time unrealized dream of his. Neruda urges Grandma to come visit so they can travel together to Northern China and "drink fermented goat's milk and appreciate the Gobi desert's monotonous garb."

Paper
NM
JG24210

HARALD SZEEMANN'S DIRTY NAPKIN (1971)

The napkin used by Harald Szeemann in the restaurant "La Vache" in Kassel. Used to remove sour cream from his beard just before he scolded Alina Szapocznikow for asking if he could help provide funding for the production of a large abdominal sculpture for documenta V. Szeemann had shouted his response: "You have to get the resources and realize the project yourself, and then, and only then, will we decide whether it should appear in documenta or not!" Alina stood up and left in protest, but Grandma was able to grab the napkin before following her out the door.

Paper napkin and sour cream
G- (mold on the napkin)
JG24211

LEE AND PINK'S SPRAY TIP (1979)

A New York spray tip from an aerosol spray can used by Lee and Pink. Bestowed on Grandma by Fred Brathwaite aka Fab 5 Freddy at an opening in the Marlborough Gallery in New York. Freddy has written on a thank you card: "Let's love as our Greek forefathers did. No scooby-dooing around this time!"

Plastic, paint
G+ (the spray tip is clogged)
JG24212

PHOTOGRAPH OF GRANDMA AND SERGE SABARSKY (1947)

Taken on a hot day in July in the Upper West Side of New York, when Grandma and Serge were on their way to Zabar's to buy goods for a dinner party with Erich Heckel, Oskar Kokoschka and Max Beckmann. Grandma has bought a red chilli that most likely rates at a million Scoville degrees, and which she will serve to Kokoschka in revenge for the portrait that he painted of her in which she looks like a tuberculosis patient.

Black & white photograph
VG+
JG24213

GUSTAV METZGER'S ARNICA MASSAGE OIL (1966)

Following "The Destruction in Art Symposium" in London, Grandma was so worn out from the iconoclastic energy that Metzger offered to give her a massage with his special formula for arnica oil. While he was at it, Grandma was able to snatch the bottle and store it in her bra.

Arnica oil and a glass container
VG- (Note: half full bottle)
JG24214

LEE SCRATCH PERRY'S CHRISTMAS CARD (1984)

Christmas greetings written in pen by Perry's Swiss wife, Mireille. She writes that Lee urges her to "Convey all my love to the polar bears and moose of Norway." The card is signed in pencil by "Pipecock Jackxon & Mireille"

Paper
NM (like new)
JG24215

ADOLPH GOTTLIEB'S RED WINE BOTTLE CORK (1932)

Originating from a light Chianti that Grandma and the young artists, Mark Rothko and Adolph Gottlieb, shared together in Houston in 1932. Grandma recalled that Rothko expounded solely upon "tragedy, ecstasy and destruction" as artistic motifs, whilst Gottlieb only talked about "zen Buddhism and the positioning of hands." During the course of the conversation, Gottlieb etched the words "Lux et Oriente" into the cork with an unidentified pointed object.

Cork, red wine
G+
JG24216

Dear Gustimoldo

Another day alone in the house, but this one is different from all the others. I am expecting the first delivery of black signs. Over 800 of them were cleared by customs yesterday and the shipping office promised me that the delivery would be sent from the harbour today. I am sitting on the veranda steps, wiling away the time by reading through the black book. Going back to the original text—our own Dead Sea Scrolls—provides a deeper understanding of what it is we have tasked ourselves with.

When I asked you what you actually intended with the black signs project, you responded in parables and aphorisms, delivered in the mode of an urban sermon. One favourite anecdote of yours was that, as a child, you once dared to swallow two thumb tacks. When your mother discovered what you had consumed, she panicked and was sure that a painful death was in store. But the neighbour, who had come running at the sounds of alarm, quickly regained composure and walked quietly back across the hall. She returned after a few minutes' time with a tin of asparagus and urged you to eat the slimy, white stalks and to drink the salty brine. Then you were required to stand up straight for one hour. You didn't understand any of it and neither, most likely, did your mother, but the neighbour insisted that there was no cause for worry and her calm demeanour convinced you both. Within your stomach, the asparagus stalks disintegrated into thousands of small threads that wound themselves around the thumb tacks, packaging them into harmless bundles. After an hour, you pressed out those two asparagus tacks as your mother nearly swooned. You were both witnesses to one of those very rare old wives' tales that worked.

Human children swallow thousands of thumb tacks and dream of producing a sword. Let our black signs be the twines of asparagus that bind together these thousands of scattered thoughts and visions into a single, swooping sword.

Did you mean that our black signs would guide our society's current, splintered reality back toward a single dominant worldview that would unite and heal?

Another parable that you often referred to was one about polar bears on Svalbard, a true Gustimoldo classic. You had once seen a television programme about a guide who sold tours guaranteeing a polar bear sighting. The television team arrived and planned to follow five Italian tourists from Naples to their meeting with the polar bears. On the first day, they set out in a boat that moved steadily up along the coastline but there weren't any polar bears to be seen. The next day, they started off on snow scooters from Spitsbergen, but returned eight hours later without the desired result. On the third and final day before their departure, many in the group were upset that the bears hadn't shown up to their promised appointment. "Today," promised the guide, who was in a surprisingly good mood, "you are going to see enough polar bears to make your head spin." The tourists drove in a colonnade of four-wheel drives out of the town. After only a few minutes, one could see a black knoll protruding up along the horizon of Svalbard's white plains. Little did the tourists realize that the guide was steering them toward the largest landfill in the archipelago. As they came closer, they could see some grey figures navigating the manmade heaps. The guide let out an unrestrained cheer at the discovery. There were five polar bears, including two cubs, all of them grey from the rubbish, wandering the landfill in search of food. "Here are your polar bears!" This is where the parable ended. The lesson that you extracted from this tale was not environmental in nature. Rather, you claimed that in order to be able to live in true peace, to be able to see beauty, one must seek out the grotesque, the vile, the wretched, and enter into it, embrace it wholeheartedly. There was no such artificial separation in nature, this dichotomy had been manufactured by the human race and had to be squeezed out of our marrow once and for all. The black signs would present people with the black histories so that they would finally wake up and be able, for a single moment, to look out across the boundaries toward the unfathomable. The totality of life, you claimed.

Polar bears on a landfill.

Was this the plumb line with which you measured our times, Gustimoldo?

My god.

Gustimoldo, your parables have little power over me nowadays. To me, they are like half-truths. Ideas that punch and claw from inside a sack because they will never be released and followed to their logical conclusions. It is strange for me to remember how captivated I was when you delivered these sermons. I belonged to you. But in the absence of your presence and ranting rhetoric, the parables seem empty. They are, to use one of your own expressions, "like going to a whorehouse and discovering that they only offer porn on DVD." You have failed me.

I turn to the black book now to find the strength I need for our task.

Dear Gustimoldo

I am sitting in the library looking over all the jutegnask that Grandma pilfered over a period of a hundred years. A photo of Grandma on the wall catches the eye. It is from the time that she posed as a nude model at Ekely in 1913. According to one leading researcher on Edvard Munch, his oil paintings "On the Sofa" and "Weeping Nude" were painted during these sessions, and the woodcut "Towards the Forest" can be seen as Munch's personal tribute to Grandma. The photograph shows her running naked through the garden whilst playing with Munch's St. Bernard, Bamse. Although she was only 11 years old, Grandma looks like she is 24. She adapted to whoever was in her presence. When she reached the age of 90, most people believed she wasn't a day over 30, and Grandma used to only date men who had been born after she turned 70. My gaze turns to a quadratic wooden box with a glass lid containing a dried out slice of bread with mould. This is all that remains from a nonsensical portrait that Giacomo Balla made of Grandma at a sidewalk cafe in Milan in 1923, using a bread slice and mortadella as raw materials. Next to this is a hospitality rider from the Billy Eckstine Band that Grandma worked for in the capacity of costume and makeup designer during their tour of 31 states in 1945. Below this hangs a faded brown photograph of her and Louis Ferdinand Céline at a café in Brussels in 1934. Grandma is smiling directly into the camera, while Céline is gesturing violently toward a waiter, accusing him of having put too many ice cubes in his pastis. Framed in a plastic bag hangs a handwritten bill attached with a thumb tack to the wall. This is from when Grandma, Philip Glass, Richard Serra, John Cale and Steve Reich ate lunch at Harold's on Lexington and 45th Street in 1966. Reich treated Grandma to the feast in appreciation of her having introduced him to the human rights activist Truman Nelson, who had commissioned a new work from him in connection to the Harlem Six trial. The thing that remains consistent throughout every photograph of Grandma is that she either appears completely happy or completely miserable. If she is in top form, then the whole room celebrates, but if she is down in the dumps, everyone else is plunged into Hades. Grandma had the power to affect groups of people around her into entering into exactly the same mood that she was in at any moment. An acquaintance of Grandma once told me a story that confirmed this suspicion. On a day in May in 1951, Grandma ate a mediocre fish au gratin at a tavern in Malmö. She became so ill tempered that a thunderstorm gathered overhead which stretched from Österlen all the way to Kristianstad. Upon which she declared: "To the Cirque Nouveau in Moscow!" Eighteen hours later, a dozen of her closest friends and family sat together with her on a train between Finland and the Soviet Union. And three days after the fateful fish gratin, Grandma saw a brown bear riding fearlessly on the back of a horse in the Kircha Theatre in Moscow, accompanied by a sonata by Hindemith in the background, and everything was well once again. I remember her galloping around with me on her shoulders at Theatercaféen in Oslo, requesting the orchestra up on the veranda to play me the birthday song even though it wasn't my birthday. She ordered up five main courses from among the menu's most expensive for me while I looked, from my perch atop her shoulders, across the street to the McDonald's, where one could have bought fifty hamburgers for what she paid in tips. But one didn't get much time to dwell on things where Grandma was concerned. In the next moment, the entire restaurant broke into a Parisian Polka because Grandma had told them to.

There was no one who knew Grandma well. As soon as anyone began to get close to her, Grandma retreated to the next man, next direction, next style, next country, next course of studies, next political movement. She could alter her appearance from one day to the next, so that no one could ever be sure whether it was her or someone else traipsing around the house. She would look like a well-travelled blond trade union leader from Germany on one day, and a fragile poet of the Lettrist-movement held captive in the far reaches of Eastern Europe on the next. There were people who stubbornly insisted to have been in her company in Memphis or Melbourne at the same point in time that she had in actuality been present with me in Oslo. Of course, this wasn't really a surprise. I sometimes suspected that Grandma was actually multiple people in one, or that she wasn't a person at all. She was a willpower, a genesis, an obsession, an ancient fertility myth that originates in multiple cultures simultaneously. Against the world's violent sterility, she engendered the artistic act of creation. She refused to open up to just anyone. Her power could not be disturbed.

Let there be light, without the exclamation.

There are a number of poetry collections in the library, declarations of love from horndogs and Nobel Prize winners. The names that I read on the bindings are Olav Angell, Ingeborg Bachmann, Jackson Mac Low, Ján Ondruš and Sylvia Plath. I take out one of the thin pamphlets from the recessed bookshelf. It appears to be a first edition of Federico García Lorca's *Poema del cante jondo* with an inscription written across the table of contents: "To my sun. To my bowels." A shoebox on the shelf contains several rarities, among them an envelope with Grandma's hunting trophies. This is also where one finds a biting piece of hate mail from Anna Akhmatova, who politely asks Grandma to go where the sun doesn't shine after Modigliani had fallen head over heels in love with her in Paris in 1914. The same envelope holds an insistent letter from Hannah Arendt urging Grandma to keep her paws off of "my little lovepony Heidegger." At the bottom of the box is a shopping list for Grandma, written by Samuel Beckett. They were lovers when Grandma studied literature and English under his instruction at Trinity in Dublin in 1930. I remember that Grandma once said that "the duckling, Samuel" became so beautiful as the years passed, and was very photogenic, but that he had looked like "a grey-haired shrew in his younger days." The shopping list states:

* One pair of black flat leather shoes
* A turtleneck sweater (preferably cashmere)
* Puncture repair kit for the bicycle
* Two bottles of Guinness (for god's sake not Buckfast)

The shoebox also contains a notebook from the Black Panther meeting that she and a friend, Torun Bülow-Hübe, participated in at the Moderna Museet in 1971 during the exhibition "Utopias & Visions". Attached to the top notebook spirals is a bolt that she took off of the museum's Bucky Dome on the island of Skeppsholmen. At the top of the bookshelf, just near the ceiling, lined up in a row, are pieces of art signed by Benny Motzfeldt and Ulla Brantenberg, each of them gifts from the time Grandma was a leader for "Alpha Borealis," the spiritual meditation group of Norwegian female glass and textile artists. On a plastic mannequin next to the bookshelf there is a complete Catalan bullfighting costume for girls, a gift from Tor Ulven on her 89th birthday. To the left of the triangular bull-fighting hat hangs a picture taken at the housewarming party of Imelda and Juan Marcos in New York, in which Grandma, Keith Haring and Tony Bennett dance as Larry Levan spun his tunes. I start to lose the overview among this terrain of jutegnask occupying the library, and to get it back I focus on the tilted photograph in a silver frame that shows Ferdinand Hodler and Grandma in front of the painting "Le Bucheron / Wood Cutter", from his solo exhibit in Marseille in 1917. Smiling widely, she mirrors the wood cutter's pose with his arms held high above his head, ready to swing.

Grandma got pregnant when she was 61 years old. She bore my mother at the age of 62. She never told anyone who the father was. Gustimoldo, we joked that my mother was the art world's Freddy Krueger. Her father was a thousand crazy artists, philosophers, cultural leaders, architects, critiques and musicians. But Mother had neither knives for hands nor a black and red striped sweater, and she didn't resemble an artist-type either. Rumours had it that my grandfather was Grandma's dentist, a short anaemic man who was always invited to Grandma's gatherings. He would sit there alone on the sofa and eat the herring that Grandma, in wintertime as well as in summer, would procure for him. The dentist wouldn't prepare it in the usual way, with mustard, sour cream and dark bread, but would rather suck on the herring with a far-off look in his eyes. Even if he were sitting next to a cultural minister or Adorno, he seemed unaffected by what was taking place around him. Even when Grandma would stare him into the wall with an inappropriate, passionate gaze, he would continue sucking on the herring and stare silently back. It was clear where his priorities lay. My alleged grandfather seldom spoke, but used every opportunity to remark to his conversational partners, especially if they were of the younger generation of teeth owners, that one must take care not to get an infection in the gums. The only time he ever became animated was once when he described this type of infection as "the modern-day plague." For a fleeting moment, there was a glimmer in his eyes. According to rumours, Grandma was fervently in love with the dentist, the most punctilious man in the western hemisphere.

Her love was never returned.

Wherever I look around the house, I see fragments of this power to act at any moment, to initiate, to experience and see. On a music stand in the corner, which she received from Krzysztof Komeda in Warsaw in 1955, there is a score that one of the boys in Tangerine Dream composed for her when she accompanied William Friedkin and the band to Costa Rica for their recording of "The Sorcerer". Behind me, above the sofa, a large poster of the Gorilla Girls hangs next to a postcard from Jacques Villon, who writes that his brother, Marcel Duchamp "was, in truth a lousy chess player, a poseur." There is no end to the jutegnask, Gustimoldo. I stand up and walk over to the veranda door. Olav Strømmes's lawn mower is in the garden, gleaming. On the hubcaps, there are large cracks in the black paint from hitting a rock. The cracks remind one suspiciously of his paintings, perhaps not a coincidence? In the corner of the garden is the simple pavilion that Arne Korsmo and Mies van der Rohe built for Grandma during one rainy after party in 1966. The odd pyramid-like structure of the roof is an addition that Oscar Niemeyer drew up after the original flat roof collapsed beneath the weight of snow during the winter of 1971.

Everywhere, indications of her unflagging determination. It's almost unbearable.

Gustimoldo, you never asked me why I grew up with Grandma? The answer is not easy. I never met my parents. I have been told by some that my mother so vehemently hated Grandma and her jutegnask collection that, in defiance, she signed up for a career in the military on the day of her eighteenth birthday. My mother moved away to the northern part of the country, as far away as she could get, and settled on the military base on the Varanger Peninsula at the border of Russia. This provided her with a home, a job, and a safe distance from Grandma. She didn't desire anything more. One year later, she became pregnant by a nameless military employee. My mother had made the rounds in the military camp and my father must have been someone who didn't want to be labelled a cuckold. It didn't matter, anyhow. She died nine months later of a relentless blood infection during childbirth and there was no one to sign the paternity forms. According to the doctor, just as Mother's pulse ebbed away, one could hear the sound of a car engine idling outside. He peered out of the window into the winter night and in the middle of the snowdrift, spotted a small blue Peugeot with its high beams on and two figures heading toward the barracks with a determined stride. These were Grandma and her best friend, Louise Bourgeois who had driven from Oslo with the sole purpose of demanding to take me into their custody. Facing the head-on icy winds and pitch black night, Grandma and Bourgeois drove south again with me swaddled tightly in a hospital blanket.

The only time that Grandma ever really behaved was when

she watched films starring the actress Bette Davis. Especially one film in particular, called *All About Eve,* which she watched over and over again. For each quip that Bette Davis would say, Grandma would nod her head emphatically and repeat: "Bette Davis portrays life in all its facets. All its facets." When Grandma ended up at the nursing home, she no longer wanted to watch Bette Davis. She would snort and spit rainbow-coloured gobs at the nurses if they wouldn't put on a new MacGyver episode. Then she would plunge into the screen to watch the hero save the world bit by bit. In her last days, she didn't speak much, not even to me. She lay still and breathed through her mouth. But with a sudden lurch, she could jump up in her hospital bed and snap at the nurses if they didn't do as she asked: "I have slept with Manfred Eicher in a cellar in Düsseldorf, so you'd better watch out! I was also Larry Gagosian's girlfriend, and they are going to come get you, they are. I doubt you've ever been to San Simeon with Randolph Hearst, have you, and eaten zebra tenderloin with Charlie Chaplin—but I have!" The vigour that flowed through her veins never quite ran out, there was always a single drop left that could get her going. The last image I have of Grandma is when she was carted away from the TV screen in order to sit at lunch with the other residents of the nursing home. She issued a cry from deep in her chest, the way that only old people without vocal chords can do: "MacGyver, come back."

I realize as I write this letter, Gustimoldo, that Grandma's life and work is the complete antithesis of the black signs. It isn't impossible to imagine that thousands of the blue signs we see erected around the country, describing the cultural and historical significance of the adjoining locations, can be attributed to her actions, but nor can we ignore the fact that many of the black signs' complaints were brought about in her wake as well. Under her motto "Let there be light!" Grandma travelled the world restlessly for 108 years in the belief that every individual, in their innate creativity, could participate in a universal morality and intellectual self-realisation. That it was possible to achieve a perfect world. Humanity was obligated to strive towards beauty and truth, even if we weren't sure how to define what these were.

Everyone was on the road toward Jerusalem, Arkadia, Valhalla or Blokksberg.

The most important thing was that we were on our way.

Dear Gustimoldo

A happy day. The first black signs have arrived and there are no words for how utterly perfect they are! They are stacked on large pallets in the garden, wrapped in plastic. Even though it snowed in the night, I ran out wearing only my stockings and climbed up to the top of the stacks. After clawing away the packaging, I was able to glimpse the first black sign. And I can only say: we are talking quality. They are characterized in every way by exquisite craftsmanship. The signs have been cast in solid iron with three coats of paint atop the black and white base. The paint has been so evenly distributed that you can easily see yourself reflected in the signs' surface. The cutter that the printer used must have been adjusted to the millimetre. The edges are so cleanly cut, and you can run your finger across the whole without feeling a single irregularity. I have just been in the kitchen weighing one of the black signs, and can say that the printers have delivered as promised here as well. The weight is exactly 1795 grams.

Congratulations, Gustimoldo!

I have even scrubbed the attic so that it will be spic and span for storing the signs. The task of being down on all fours scouring the floorboards as a kind of welcoming ritual felt very natural. Watching the dust of Grandma's jutegnask being washed away added to the good gut feeling. And now you must promise not to laugh: I have already tested out the best method for hanging up the signs. I purchased various types of drills, clamps, and superglue and have started a list of which method is best suited to various surfaces. My rapidly increasing statistics indicate that the signs will primarily be fastened to marble, iron, stone and glass surfaces within the city. One should also expect a bit of plastic and aluminium, but these surfaces are in the minority. Of utmost importance is figuring out the most effective and qualitative methods for affixing the signs so that they can remain hanging over a long period. The best option is to attach them so solidly that their removal would cause serious damage to the underlying surface. One topic that we may want to consider is whether to invest in some kind of sound muffler. The noise when I drill into the surface and hammer in the fasteners is unbelievably loud. We cannot fulfil our task if we risk being arrested each time we go to hang a sign. I will get back to you when I start seeing some results from my experiments. We will let the statistics do the talking.

So, Gustimoldo. The black signs have arrived and the auctions are underway—and just when was it that you were thinking of turning your wagon toward home again? Need I remind you that you are a part of this, that we initiated and planned the whole thing together down to the last detail? Even by our low standards, this is far below par. Two people are required to hang the signs, one to do the mounting and one to drive. People are going to think we are burglars, vandals or something worse. I hope you are aware of your duty, for I am planning to send letter after letter, and even more letters, to keep you updated. These words shall chase you round the earth on silent wings.

The only thing I have left are the black signs.

Come home, Gustimoldo.
Come forth, Gustimoldo.

PS! After a day spent stacking signs in the attic, I have

concluded that there should be a particular equilibrium between the amount of jutegnask that is being mailed out of the house, and the signs that are coming in. Wherever there was once jutegnask, there is now a black sign.

PPS! The auctions are taking off, Gustimoldo! People are lobbing money at us to get their hands on some jutegnask. I'm beginning to doubt whether our initial research is enough. There is the possibility that we may have to print many more signs than we originally thought. I am going to assume this and get back to you. As I said, the statistics will do the talking.

LUDWIG WITTGENSTEIN'S RUCKSACK (1914)

Grandma was an invaluable supporter and sounding board for Wittgenstein during his time in Norway. She assisted him both in acquiring land and with accruing a workforce for building his cabin in Skjolden at the Lustra fjord. Grandma borrowed Ludwig's rucksack, which she and G.E. Moore needed to carry his books that would be shipped from Christiania to Cambridge. She never gave it back.

Textile and metal
VG- (cocoa spots on the base of the pack)
JG101343

PHOTOGRAPH OF GRANDMA, MOINHOI AND KLAUS KINSKI IN THE HARAJUKU-DISTRICT (1976)

In the photograph, taken by Grandma using a self-timer, the group is eating Takoyaki (Japanese octopus balls) in a fast food restaurant near the Harajuku district of Tokyo. Moinhoi and Kinski are wearing their usual extravagant leather suits and fur hats. Grandma has burned her tongue on one of the Takoyaki balls and is holding her red tongue, which is protruding out toward the camera lens.

Coloured photograph
VG+
JG101344

SNOOP DOGG'S HOT DOG NAPKIN (2008)

Grandma took the napkin when Calvin Cordozar Broadus, aka Snoop Dogg, launched his new brand "Doggy Snacks". Among other products, he unveiled a foot-long hot dog, the "Snoop Hot Dogg", for which Grandma was flown in as a witness and to lend an air of cultural gravity to the event. Broadus burst into tears when Grandma called "Doggy Snacks" the most beautiful thing to happen to African American cultural life since Charles Burnett's neo-realistic blaxploitation film, "Killer of Sheep".

Cotton
VG-
JG101345

SIGNED COPY OF THE LITERARY MAGAZINE "ORPHEU" (1915)

A group dedication from the Portuguese writers Fernando Pessoa, Mário de Sá-Carneiro and José de Almada Negreiros with their thanks to Grandma for having distributed their magazine to a few Nordic retailers and for arranging a mention in the *Morgenposten* newspaper. Pessoa writes that he owes Grandma a steaming hot bowl of Julian soup at Martinho da Arcade next time she visits Lisbon.

Paper with staple
NM/VG+
JG101346

ARNOLD BODE'S BROKEN GLASSES (1964)

At documenta III, Joseph Beuys' son Wenze lost his ice cream outside of the Fridericianum. Arnold Bode bent down to pick it up without noticing that Mr Beuys was also bending down. They collided. Beuys lost his hat, Bode lost his glasses, and both lay sprawled out on the ground. In the ensuing chaos, Beuys' hat was restored to him by Werner Haftmann while Grandma picked up the glasses and hid them in her back pocket.

Horn rimmed glasses (unknown make)
G- (broken glass on the left lens)
JG101347

PHOTOGRAPH OF MILES DAVIS, JIMI HENDRIX AND GRANDMA (1970)

The photo is taken with a self-timer and portrays a meeting in New York in which Grandma introduced Hendrix to Davis while suggesting that they should collaborate. The Columbia studio was booked and music was written, but Hendrix died on September 18th of the same year, only two days before the scheduled uptake. Davis' newly written material for their planned collaboration later ended up on his album *Live-Evil*.

Coloured photograph
NM
JG101348

ROBERT CREELEY'S EYEPATCH (1972)
Originating from Robert Creeley's and Jan Erik Vold's lecture series in Oslo and Bergen in 1972. After the reading at Club 7, Grandma and her friend Sidsel Paaske wanted to dance with their dates. During a fearlessly morbid séance on the dance floor, Grandma bit off Creeley's eyepatch and rolled it up under her tongue. She never returned it.

Cotton
VG+
JG101349

PHOTOGRAPH OF GRANDMA, CAROLEE SCHNEEMAN, JIM DINE AND YOKO ONO AT THE MORI ART MUSEUM (2004)
The group is dancing to Toshiki Kadomatsu's classic *I Can't Stop the Night* with green martinis in their hands on the roof of the skyscraper. Photographer unknown, most likely Grandma's self-timer.

Coloured photograph
VG (a bit out of focus)
JG101350

TEST PRINT OF KLUSTER'S KLOPFZEICHEN (1970)
Across the white album cover, a stamp in blue ink states "Musterplatte. Copyright Schwann". An inscription from Hans-Joachim Roedelius to Grandma in the upper left cor-

ner reads: "Dear one. Thanks a million for helping Oskar with the ground fault in the mixing desk in Godorf. PS! I wish you didn't understand German so you wouldn't have to hear these hallelujahs."

Vinyl, cardboard cover
M-
JG101351

LETTER FROM MOHSEN MAKHMALBAF AND ABBAS KIAROSTAMI (1971)

In the letter, both of them thank Grandma for her tireless promotion of Farrokhzâd's films and for the pioneering work she has done to exalt their common idol in the West. The letter ends with, "A cherry of love to you, greetings Mohsen and Abbas."

Paper
VG+
JG101352

DOLLY PARTON'S DISPOSABLE TOOTHBRUSH (2004)

Originating from Grandma's visit to "Dollyland" in 2004. Parton and Grandma went camping in the Smoky Mountains together with their mutual friend, Judy Ogle. When Ogle and Parton went for a morning swim in a glacial pond, Grandma took the opportunity to requisition some selected objects from their toiletries bags, among them this flimsy toothbrush.

Plastic
VG+
JG101353

ANDRÉ MALRAUX' CASINO CHIPS (1951)

Casino chips from Grandma and Malraux' romantic getaway in Monaco, where they dashed from casino to casino. Rumour has it that it was on this trip that Grandma persuaded Malraux to become a valuable sponsor for directors centred around the editorial staff of the magazine "Cahiers du cinéma", that she planted the concept of a house of culture in Malraux' head and encouraged him to invest significant time in the idea's development so that it might "spread outwards across Europe, like the Middle Ages' white cloak of churches, and thereby represent the redemption of the individual on a secular basis."

Plastic
M-
JG101354

PHOTOGRAPH OF GRANDMA, IANNIS XENAKIS, EDGAR VARÉSE, LE CORBUSIER AND EDVARD OMSEN HEIBERG (1958)

Grandma and the quartet posed together with the CEO of Philips and his 23 engineers who contributed to the work "Poème Èlectronique" at the World Exhibition in Brussels in 1958. Corbusier is staring meanly at the architect Heiberg, who Grandma had brought with her to Brussels, since on the previous evening he had remarked—a little too loudly—that Corbusier's drawings were characterized by a "delusional Lautrec-streak".

Black and white photograph
NM
JG101355

HAAKEN CHRISTENSEN'S STRAW AND PHOTOGRAPH (2007)

The photograph portrays Grandma, Nicolaus Widerberg and Bjørn Sigurd Tufta next to Christensen's deathbed. In the background, Frank Brunner can be seen holding a magnum champagne bottle with a pink straw protruding from it, from which Haaken Christensen, weakened but satisfied, is taking multiple sips.

Digital coloured photograph and pink plastic straw
VG+
JG101356

FABRIC FROM YAYOI KUSAMA'S FASHION SHOW (1968)

Textile remains from clothing that Grandma sewed for Kusama's fashion show in Kusama Studio Tokyo, which consisted of colourful, knee-length dresses with large folds in the sleeves. A note attached to one piece of fabric is from Kusama, thanking Grandma for all of her help. She writes that she is really looking forward to the after party where her male assistants will be in attendance, if only she manages to keep her head above water.

Velvet, cotton, plastic buttons, paper
VG-
JG101357

HANS AND HANNAH RYGGEN'S GARDEN HOSE (1961)

The foursome Grandma, Pauline Hall and the Ryggen couple arranged a dinner party at Ørlandet after a New Music concert in Trondheim during which, among other things, Arne Nordheim's piece "Aftonland" was performed. On the next day, Grandma and Pauline helped to put the garden in order. While her friend clipped the hydrangeas, Grandma clipped off a piece of the garden hose, coiled it up and put it into her purse.

Piece of black rubber garden hose
VG+
JG101358

HUGO BALL'S DADA MANIFESTO (1961)

Pierre Restany's personal copy of Ball's Dada manifesto from 1916. This copy was used by Restany as he wrote his own manifesto "40 Degrees Above the Dada Zero" for Galleri J, Paris in 1961. When Grandma was working as the picture editor of the exhibition catalogue, she coincidentally forgot to return the manifesto to Restany.

Sheets of paper in a leather portfolio
G+ (several red pen marks throughout)
JG101359

RAMMELLZEE AND K-ROB'S BEAT BOP WITH A COVER BY JEAN-MICHEL BASQUIAT (1983)

Grandma's copy of the test print of *Beat Bop,* later released by Tartown Records, which she received from Vincent Gallo in 1984. Gallo bowed and thanked her for so gallantly brokering peace between Rammellzee and Basquiat, and not least for getting Jean-Michel to forget about the terrible verses he originally wanted to include in the song.

Vinyl with a cardboard cover
VG+
JG101360

Dear Gustimoldo

So you have decided to abandon our project? Let me conjure up your face so you can see yourself.

Come forth, Gustimoldo.

Can you remember the day that we began writing the history of the black signs? I was at Our Saviour's Cemetery as you came up along Ullevålsveien with your long, gigantic steps. You reigned yourself in as some school girls walked by and enthusiastically proceeded to hand out your business cards. I left you to it. I was some meters behind you and could hear a humming sound, a sentence you kept repeating to yourself: "Long term investments are important. Yes, long term investments are important." I touched you on the shoulder and, as expected, you had disappeared into another reality. The darkness of your pupils extended far beyond their boundaries, black on black, encircled by an even darker outline. You paid me no heed and peeled off toward St. Hanshaugen, where people lay strewn out across the summer grass. The sun was directly above us, pressing down its warmth. The teenage girls lifted their heads every other minute to check whether they had achieved any obvious tan on their skin. Three children paused in their war between the plastic boats guarding the river and began a search and rescue party for a croquet ball that someone had hit into the pond. You settled down on the lawn, tore up one piece of grass after the other, ripped them into equally sized bits and spread them gently across the ground. You were observing. The only thing one could hear between the sounds of children laughing and the rushing water, was the sound of your inhalations through your nose. You wheezed and sputtered on that summer day like an old TV

set that someone forgot to turn off at night. Then, in an ir-
revocable act of willpower, you informed Oslo:

I can't stand it anymore!

You suddenly pounced onto a bikini clad creature and began sticking your fingers into any possible opening without discrimination. Gustimoldo—you resembled an overgrown infant who, shortly after birth gazes at the outside
world, does an about-face, loops the umbilical cord around
and dives back in again. I reacted by tackling you. Welcome
back to the world, you are going to be here for many years.
As you lay writhing, I explained to the crowd that had begun to gather that I was a therapist at an institution you
had managed to break out of. I pointed at a random house,
informed them that any inquiries could be directed there,
but in the meanwhile I would need to administer your
sedatives. I locked your arms into a strange grip that I had
once seen in a film and pulled you away from the scene.
Realizing the absurdity of the situation, we both snickered
together for a few seconds before hightailing it around the
corner. Bislett Bingo was our hideout. After we secured a
few Bingo cards to share, I expected some measure of relief
to settle in, but your restlessness only increased when you
realized that Bingo wasn't exactly your cup of tea. You began dreaming about what you would use any winnings for
and wouldn't share your thoughts with anyone else. After
only a few numbers had been called, you began screaming:
"Bingo! Bingo! Bingo! Bingo!" The local regulars looked at
you sceptically, and threw their cards absentmindedly into
the trash. The lucky winner, you walked up to the counter
to collect your prize. The announcer quickly disproved
your winning, as none of the squares of your card had been
crossed off. The Bingo players, who are not really known

for being the most empathetic people, began murmuring that something like this had never happened before, it was a downright scandal. The mood began turning dangerously sour and only increased proportionally when you began yelling: "Bingo! Bingo! Bingo! Bingo!" while running around the room swiping glue sticks and packets of cigarettes from the tables. I once again assumed my role as the environmental therapist.

We were in and out of bars for the rest of that summer evening. Or rather, you were in and out of a psychosis for the rest of the summer evening. What a shitty companion. To top it all off, you were in top form for delivering your sermons, and I spent every half hour searching for you. I most often found you standing in front of a queue at a nightclub, a cash machine at a 7-Eleven or at a dance floor PA system, where you attempted to unplug all the power cables in order to draw attention to your own speech. These damned urban sermons of yours, Gustimoldo, were always accompanied with a warm-up routine in which you stretched your facial muscles and wagged your tongue up and down, while taking large steps back and forth to ensure yourself that you were not weightless. You stuck your nose into the air and pulled your trousers high up above your waist so that your torso appeared unnaturally short. This was the sign that you were ready to start preaching. Thank god that you weren't ever a man of the church, Gustimoldo! In the end, you found yourself at the fountain in the Youngstorget Square, which was the highest point in the area. The show was well underway when I arrived. You were just in the middle of a speech about the world's intrinsic nihilism, that our contemporary society was everything that our parents had fought for, so why shouldn't they all just leave it alone, settle down and enjoy some chewing tobacco. "If this is everything we can fight for, if this is the first prize, then we say no thank you! Our generation would rather sit still!" You could switch topics like no other. Now you began to talk about the minutes between 3:00 and 3:15, where the fate of human society was decided, "Where fates are sealed and men return home to either eternal glory or to humiliation!" You meant with or without a pussy on your arm. The crowd hollered. You started in on a sermon in which you compared the Financial Minister's speech with the new oracle of Delphi. And then about Max Manus. And then about housing prices. And immigration. And vaccines. And oil. And social security. And the purge of collaborators after WWII. And gender. And immigration. And the export of arms.

A string of pearls.

After an hour, I was the only one still listening. In the other listeners' eyes, you had gone from being a charming oddball to a bullied child with access to automatic weapons. You cast a dazzling smile at me, held two fingers in the air and concluded with the prophetic challenge, "Stop being relative, start getting wasted!" that resounded across the square. In a mixture of intoxication from sermon-giving and a lack of medications, you collapsed and plopped into the fountain for a nightly plunge. When I was finally able to lift your head up, your face was neither green, blue or white, but rather brown, as if a mixture of vomit and blood were pressing against you from the inside but couldn't get out through your skin. As the ambulance was on its way, I went through your pockets to find out what you had been taking. I found only stacks of business cards and a tin of raspberry pastilles. Thanks to your odd appearance, the ambulance drivers merely thought you were a junkie.

They hit you in the face and screamed into your ear that they were going to inject you with a serum and that they expected you to come back from the dead. But you simply lay there, still and brown as the month of March.

It was an indefinable feeling of helplessness I felt at the ER. I thought what I always think when finding myself inside institutions: "Now you're going to have to feel something." I don't know, in any case there wasn't much in store for me. I set out on an expedition along the corridors of the first floor and for awhile was absorbed in what was going on there awhile. A man from Ethiopia collapsed to the floor when the pain in his legs was too much to bear. A girl in a wheelchair stood up and offered the wheelchair to the nurse. A sick child lay on a sofa in the waiting room. The colour of his skin contrasted with the Lego blocks he was clasping. In the corner, a patient with a cap on sat reading a pamphlet about public support for wig subsidies that he had received from the doctor. The second room was reserved for a group of drug addicts and gypsies who had figured out that taking a number in the ER waiting room was equivalent to one night of free, warm shelter. My attention was drawn toward the counter, where an impatient teenager railed at a nurse behind the window and raised his voice with each sentence. His tone became more and more aggressive as the woman repeated: "You must be eighteen years old, seventeen is not old enough. Even at Ullevål or Aker hospital, they can't help you with something like that." Someone mentioned that the young man wanted to get himself sterilized and had been thrown out multiple times throughout the day, but had returned each time. My heavy thoughts were gone. There were so many outrageous types of life encapsulated in this building that it was impossible not to get carried away. I went up one floor and arrived at the patient cafeteria. A man with an eyepatch sat gobbling his meal consisting of brown sauce and a heap of slick boiled institutional potatoes. I stood next to the soda machine and struck up a chat with one of your nurses. She asked if things were okay, and I answered: "Life is like a river, it runs." She wasn't familiar with the expression and looked at me kindly as she said, "It is so nice that you are waiting for him. We will tell him that you are out here whenever he wakes up, which isn't often." Encouraged, I had to ask how one could work in the ER, didn't it make one lose their appetite for one's own private life, since the job was so exciting? She dismissed my question as strange, took a sip from her soda bottle and said she had to return to duty. If anyone ever feels depressed, I would highly recommend taking a trip to the ER or to a hospital. You'll see as much love of life here in a single day as you will see in a whole year in the city. And it's free. I walked on and came to a stair leading down to the cellar. After a long corridor packed to the brim with stowed public art works, I arrived at a split in my path. One way led to custodial department and the other to the medicinal combustion chamber. Before I was able to make a choice, a man wearing a security uniform came over and asked whether I was looking for anything in particular. I was sent back to the ER via a lift and directed to the correct floor. You were laying inside of the room, Gustimoldo, looking almost like a corpse. Your eyes were opened. Your mouth closed. Your nose was the only thing in touch with the world around you.

Everything was a knife.

All I could do was to act like I couldn't help you. I got a glass of water for you, the only respectable thing that a person can do in a situation like this. Your sleeping was agitated, like a dog in the sun. A few hours later, you got up out of bed. It was four in the morning. You were certain that someone had kidnapped you and mumbled that we were a gang of organ thieves and terrorists who planned to operate bombs into or out of your body. You bolted suddenly, taking with you a drip stand and a box of plastic gloves, and ran past the reception, across the parking lot, down the slope and dove into the Akerselva river. I took a detour across the bridge and followed the path downriver along the opposite embankment. You swam quickly with the current in the direction of the Grønland neighbourhood. Where the river turned shallow, you began to crawl, going forward on hands and knees, but when the river got deeper again, you sank down and disappeared from sight. At times I was able to make out your hospital gown on the water's surface, like a turquoise dolphin jumping in the moonlight. We met at the pool near Vaterland Bridge, where you swam in circles while some passersby tried to coax you up out of the water. Others were looking for a stick or a rope, while a few security guards from the ER came and lit you up with the elongated beams of their flashlights. To this you responded by swimming toward a tunnel which led out to the Oslo fjord. I was painfully aware that the security guards were not trained in how to handle such an acute situation, and so there was only one thing to do. I jumped, fully clad, into the pool and followed you into the tunnel. When my eyes could no longer perceive nuances in the darkness, I navigated by keeping close to one of the sides of the tunnel. I removed layer after layer of my clothing as I was plunged beneath the water. Whenever I got too close to your struggles, I would stop and hold back a few meters, maintaining a safe distance. And so it continued, you swimming in a zigzagged panic ahead of me, sometimes in the wrong direction, while I followed some meters behind you. After half an hour of swimming, we could see the opening out toward Bjørvika where the sunrise above Oslo let in some light. To my great surprise, you didn't head for land to continue on foot, but continued swimming. As we passed Vippetangen, some hobby fishermen called out to us. I couldn't hear their exact words, but I think they were warning us that the boat from Denmark or the Nesodden ferry was heading straight toward us. Is it possible to swim so deeply under water that you won't get hit by those boats, and how long can one stay submerged? I turned to look back. I didn't see any ferries, only a police boat that was on its way out from the dock at City Hall. The swim strokes were more powerful now. We were halfway to Hovedøya. We flailed, thrashed, surged. With each stroke I understood more and more that this was no longer a chase. We both set our course toward the open sea and released all of the strength that we had in our bodies.

Our only goal was to get away.

When you awoke in the hospital a few days later, the first thing you did was to thank me. I was certain that you felt cheated because I hadn't just let you go to your ruin, and so I asked why.

> It's just as nice hanging around to see what will happen.

Don't you remember?

That same morning is when we decided to write the history of the black signs.

Dear Gustimoldo

Can't you remember our elation when we wrote the black histories? Gone was the tension and that endless frenetic friction between the thoughts of superior human beings and self-hatred—we were hooked, and for the first time in our lives waking up in the morning was a delight. We decided, as do so many of our generation, to go on welfare while pursuing what it was that we actually wanted to do. The early phase of our research for the black signs was to scour the libraries, public archives and the Norwegian central statistic office. We dug up any information that was connected to degradation, bankruptcy, and drowning and boat accidents. The next day, we would romp through the tabloid archives and take note of cases referring to wrongful diagnoses, escalated neighbour feuds, and bone fractures resulting from slips on the ice. Among the archives of the Norwegian Labour Inspection Authority and the Norwegian National Association of Dentistry, we were able to uncover so many dark histories that we had to order new filing cabinets to store all the files. That order doubled once we wormed our way into such hot topics like exposing WWII traitors, swine flu vaccinations, and the witch trials in northern Norway. After our brief foray into the research branch, we got on a first name basis with Oslo's antique booksellers and some resolute local historians. Sharing mugs of coffee with retired municipal politicians and resigned hospital employees became a part of our daily routine. Our research archives expanded and our days were replete with meaning. After one year working together as aspiring research partners, we decided to calibrate our methods and areas of focus and to divide our tasks in order to streamline our collection. By drawing lots, we determined that you would spend three years in the microfilm archives at the National Library with the overall tasks of mapping the black histories located in the un-digitalised national and local newspapers. My allotted task took me to NRK's radio and television archives, where I became glassy-eyed staring at every news program and talk show that had been produced on the airwaves since 1933. Do you remember that feeling of pride, Gustimoldo—that feeling of having built up an academic weight behind the history of the black signs that no one else could surpass? Although we worked in 12 hour shifts we met up each evening to have dinner together and to present our day's research results to one another. We compared our finds, noted similarities and regarded development curves in the black histories. While we ate dessert, we compiled the final lists to decide which histories were deserving of their own black sign.

Everything was to be included.

When the National Library and NRK's files had been fully ransacked, the time had come to go forth on a coronation tour. Norway's grim county archives and weary local news-papers lay ahead of us. On our tour of the local counties, we also set aside time to meet with locally well known collec-tors of extremely rare history books who were all more than willing to share their abundant knowledge with us. Such a multitude of signs! As our research work entered into its fifth year, our journeys took us to Mo i Rana and we settled down in a small hut next door to the National Library's se-curity vault within the mountain. You had become a crimi-nologist and I a cultural historian and we were astounded at how easy it was to gain access to the inner vault. The librarians and conservationists were happy that the ma-terial to which they had dedicated their lives to catalogue and protect was now being utilised. "It is so nice to see that the archive lives on, that history is being used to inform the present," one librarian said. She should have known how right she was. After our stay in the north, our work entered into its final period. A long and extensive application process, which took several years to determine, finally led to us being granted unlimited access to highly confidential material. The police, military and prison authorities were sitting on top of a gold mine of material for our black signs, and the child welfare officials, special schools, and national support groups allowed us to peruse their infinite files. While working with the latter, we came across a separate fauna of stakeholders all bearing a wealth of blame that they were only too willing to distribute. Caffeine addicts, patients with COPD, the spiritually broken, slaves to debt and people whose feet were too big.

Everyone was to be included.

The fundamental research now complete, we began on phase two. These years were marked by our determination to challenge our own methods and the retelling of history. It was not particularly ideal that the dark histories were primarily located among public records, support groups and more or less in the works of published academics. Even though it was a suppressed side of the officially accepted history hidden away in some innermost filing drawer, our goal was to show that the tendency to blame and the desire to spread it around was ingrained in all of us. After much deliberation, we came up with our idea of the "Signs of Amazement." This involved picking up the phone and calling the first and best names in the telephone book. We pretended to be representatives of opinion agencies who had been tasked with delving into the state of the country. These individuals were asked what they were particularly dissatisfied about, which wrongs had been done against them and who, if one dared ask, they would accuse? We summoned our strength and called up approximately 1,000 people per week, all of whom were more than happy to impart their black histories and to assign blame. It seemed that they had been waiting for years for this opportunity to share what had been in their hearts. There were so many unrealized dreams, grudges and pitiful marriages that we had to wash the phone every night before going to sleep. It wasn't only you, Gustimoldo, who was a legitimate heir to a fading empire. We were all legitimate heirs to a fading empire. It was seldom that anyone would put us on hold and asked us to wait. As a rule, they would quietly inform others in the room that it was an important call from their boss or from an old friend and that they had to go out for a bit. The truth was that they finally had the chance to talk behind the backs of those closest to them. When we realized the potential of the Amazement Signs as they unfolded before our eyes, we concluded that people were just thrilled about placing blame. There was not a single speck on the surface of the country that was free from blame. There was a dam far off in the distant horizon that was about ready to burst.

What a spectacle.

Seven years of our culling efforts provided us with enough black histories to produce 50,000 signs. The only thing we needed to do now was to make a graphic template, copy and paste the individual texts from our lists and send these off to the printers. Unfortunately, this was not so simple. 50,000 was not nearly enough to cover the black histories. Our research work was proceeding too slowly. A simple calculation showed that at a production rate of 8,000 signs per year, it would take 100 human lifetimes and many more than only two employees to write the entire black history. We were completists and required millions of signs before our work could be considered final. The work we had done up to this point was only a needle in the haystack in the history books. The big question was how could we write the black history more effectively? We began to despair, since we had neither resources nor solutions at our disposal and we began to realize that we were doomed to failure. However, after a few weeks, when you had been unusually absentminded and stumpy, you showed up to our daily dinner meeting with that signature smile across your face. And then you presented your solution. The sign generator! When I first heard the name, I pictured some black industrial machine spitting out mechanical clinks and clanks, squirts of oil and thick smoke. But not this time. You had programmed a generative computer program that would produce signs at a furious rate. You sat there with the generator in your hand and set it down on the kitchen table. It was a white hard disk about the size of a bar of soap. You were a former computer enthusiast, so of course you had created a computer program coded in DOS and written in C. Simply stated, our job was to feed the device with statistics about crime, accidents and generally shady happenings, which it would link up with an interactive mapping system and registry of names. By using a simple algorithm, the sign generator could create several hundred probable black histories each minute. And to reinforce its superiority, the sign generator would compile the sign-files into a zip-file which was connected to an email programme that sent the files off to the printer. It required neither oil nor maintenance. It was infinite.

To test the generator, we decided on the Viking era and plotted in the most common offences that had been committed, how the political landscape was comprised in those days and which names were popular back then. In less than one second, the generator came up with two suggestions:

BIQRN SURSSON (805-836)

It was in this spot that Biǫrn Sursson died after a dispute over a land entitlement with the Ormstunge family. He received a spear in his liver and left behind three children.

ÞŌRA HÅKONSDATTER (922-972)

Þōra's firstborn son, Sigurd, was born with a distinctly feminine appearance and possessed little chance of growing a beard. Þōra was deeply distressed for many years that her son was unable to fulfil the contemporary expectations of a man's role and that he often fell victim to harassment.

Gustimoldo, it was clear to us that the sign generator was not ethically responsible but we were certain that it was the solution we needed. Strict academic guidelines would have to be bent in the name of efficiency. However, an unforeseen issue arose due to the generator's superiority. While we had produced material in excess of 50,000 throughout our first seven years of work, we were now able to generate the same amount in less than two days. The generator worked while we slept, watched television and ate. We would feed it numbers, maps and statistics each week for some hours, and it would dutifully spit out the required sign texts. After a few months, we had in our possession the texts for 52.3 million signs. When we looked at the number, we stared at each other in fearful jubilation. This would inevitably lead to considerable financial and logistical problems when the signs would start being produced. But we didn't have the heart to pull the plug.

Dear Gustimoldo

I inhale, but am beginning to doubt whether you are also still breathing. Can't you recall our euphoria at the sight of the generator spitting out its texts? We were both afraid how it would be, how we would deal with our newfound peace and free time. I look back on that time today with a great deal of happiness. Our trips, making meals, and composing lists. We followed along in public debates, developed an interest in horticulture and were the most attentive participants in a course on the fermentation of carrots and cucumbers. At one point we even thought about getting a border collie because the colour of its fur reminded us of the black signs. That's how far we went. It's possible that I'm painting an idealised picture to lure you home. Our main interests were a bit in the margins. Take, for example, our urge to write lists. That action of putting down a number and ranking things according to our subjective taste stirred up kingly fantasies in each of us. One could argue that, at this point, half of the world's population was consumed with keeping lists and we didn't wish to lag behind. Our lists are better than yours! In retrospect, I realize that the lists weren't simply one of our contrivances. In our day and age, lists are the preferred mode of ranking knowledge, creating order and grasping the nearly ungraspable. From goal-oriented lists and to-do lists to wish lists—our society is helpless without them, and we therefore felt compelled to create a bit of disorder here as well. We spent nights ranking biographies with spelling errors, failed tests of manhood, and utterly boring vacation spots. My favourite were our lists of unmanned solariums and the most painful soft drinks on which a shrimp milkshake with vanilla topped the list. Did I forget anything essential? Of course—our list of graveyards. This masterpiece was composed one September morning as we sat at the Vestre Cemetery. Just before us lay the Karoli family's monument, which exceeded all of the standard size and angle regulations for Norwegian graveyards. Next to it was the tomb of Arne Hestenes. What a party it must be taking place there underground. As a tribute to our love of graveyards and epitaphs, we came up with this list, which I view in retrospect as the best in our line of production:

THE WORLD'S BEST GRAVEYARDS

5. *Fifth place goes to the Queens Cemetery in New York. Its placement between the roadway leading into Manhattan and the industrial area of Queens gives it a grim feeling that testifies to the classic cinematic angst of large cities and claustrophobia, even for those who are resigned to death. Bonus points for the tombstones' vertical form, like a Lilliputian version of Manhattan's skyline which serves as a backdrop to the cemetery. An honourable mention must be made for the cemetery at the abandoned Tempelhof airport in Neukölln, Berlin. When the Russians closed all roads into West Berlin, this is where the local authorities set up a graveyard nearly inside the airport, right underneath where the planes would land and take off every three minutes. The tombstones have faded from all the pollution.*

4. *In fourth place, we find the Skogskyrkogården in Stockholm. This beautiful construction, built by the architects Gunnar Asplund and Sigurd Lewerentz, was erected in the years 1915—1940.*

Skogskyrkogården is a magnificent example of a Protestant cemetery that democratically radiates the truth that we are all equal in death. The monument and meditation halls boast late modern expressive forms borrowed from Saarinen and Aalto. Better than any other monument in Northern Europe, this one demonstrates the close connection between nature and architecture and exudes a desire to create a structure that actively engages in dialogue with its surroundings. Bonus points for its status on UNESCO's world heritage sites list. Extra bonus points because Greta Garbo is buried here.

3.   *Sharing third place are the Baroque cemetery Père Lachaise in Paris and the Recoleta in Buenos Aires. Both receive points for housing a sea of famous VIPs, who may arguably be understood as the implicit architects behind the somewhat lavish designs. Much of the glory for this high placement on our list is due to the managers of the graveyards, who by their very strong restrictions about who is allowed to be buried here, demonstrate that we are all unequal in death. Honourable mention must go to St. Louis and to the La Roche in New Orleans, which could have competed with Père Lachaise and Recoleta for third place, but after the flooding in 2007 have both been redone in a style that is a bit too neatly contemporary. We have placed them on hold. (At this point we would like to draw your attention to a decision that was taken in the final stages of the committee's work on this list. Our Saviour's Cemetery in Oslo was originally settled beyond a doubt in third place,*

thereby pushing Queens Cemetery completely off the list. But since the local graveyard, which has influenced both of the panel members throughout their lives, could be viewed as subjective, we decided to leave it out. It is important to take every opportunity to underline the jury's clear independence and strong professionalism. However, this does not hinder us from writing a note about the particular relevance of Our Saviour's Cemetery. Its placement in the city centre, as a constant memento mori for Oslo's inhabitants, is a big plus. Also beneficial is that it is located close by the Gamle Aker graveyard, so you can squeeze in two cemeteries on a single visit. Another advantage is its unique geographical layout, with a mountain top at its centre, which seems to symbolize a mound of humanity attempting to stretch up out of the earth toward heaven).

2. *Following up first place, at a very strong second position, we find the abortion division of Glasnevin Graveyard in Dublin. Glasnevin is crowned with a beautiful Catholic renaissance building and several monumental tombstones and can boast several well known people who are buried among its grounds, such as Charles Stewart Parnell and Brendan Behan. Let's also not forget that the graveyard is frequently mentioned in James Joyce's Ulysses. But what makes Glasnevin remarkable, particularly by international standards, is its special division for aborted foetuses which is located at the left of the church near the main entrance. It is impossible for the common visitor not to notice. The area is filled with teddy*

bears, Lego, wind chimes, kites and computer games offered to the dead. The gravestones appear like modern mass graves: "Our Little Jimmy 1990. Our Little Louisa 1998." etc., etc. are written in long rows down across the stones. The world is full of strange compromises. When the rain pounds down and large gusts sweep through Dublin, as often happens, the wind chimes stir bewitching harmonies and the toys are heaped together in an indeterminate mass of longing and unresolved love.

1.   *And now to first place. A close victory, but none-theless convincing—Cairo's City of the Dead! At the base of the Mokattam valley near Cairo is a cluster of mighty graveyards such as the Bab el Nasr, Bab el Wazir and The Graveyard of the Giants. For centuries, the Fatimids, Abbasidians, Ayyubids and Mamluks built large villas with kitchens, bedrooms, and chambers as tombs for their family members. They were laid to rest here in mansion-like residences that allowed the family also to live there during the mourning period, lasting for forty days. The result of this is that a large stretch of villas of high quality were constructed at the graveyards in Cairo. When the housing crisis hit in the 1960s, as well as when large amounts of labour began pouring into the city from the countryside, the newcomers began taking up residence in the villas in the Mokattum valley, converting them into their homes. These new tenants never touched the coffins or defiled the spaces. On the contrary, they lived in harmony together with the dead, as if they were merely lodging with a host.*

They didn't have any problem simply living side by side with the dead. Even when the French occupation of Cairo brought with it the Western mindset that such a co-habitation was unnatural, the City of the Dead in Cairo developed into its own community with over five million inhabitants. Today, the City of the Dead has its own postal code, schools and electricity. Though the graveyard is not officially recognized as a legal place of domicile by the Egyptian government, no one has yet tried to get rid of the residents.

The graveyard is no longer a place where life ends, but a place where it begins.

Our congratulations to the City of the Dead!

In addition to our occupation of writing lists, we also dove head over heels into the world of gastronomy. It all started with one dinner where you whipped up a dish dubbed "Arabian Curiosity." You had become so fascinated by poetically named cuisine, such as the British "Stargazey Pie" and "Devils on Horseback", that you yourself wished to uphold and carry on the tradition. After extensive exploration, you decided that your favourite poetically-named dish was the German casserole "Tote Oma", or Dead Grandma, which you made into your signature dish. "Arabian Curiosity" consisted of a bed of mashed chickpeas cooked over time in apple nectar and grated ginger zest. Atop this, you arranged a cut of oxtail that had been simmered in rose hip tea and adorned with star anise foam. It tasted heavenly, Gustimoldo. On the following day, not wanting to be bested by you, I dished up "The Vanity of Rationality", roasted venison shoulder embedded with hazelnuts and mint. The meat was compressed overnight in order to thrust the hazelnuts and mint deeply into the flesh, and then it was slowly roasted at 70 degrees over 10 hours. The steak was served with a creamed rhubarb sauce and a stew of funnel chanterelles with much too much cream and acacia honey. The next day it was your turn to top me again. Show me what you got. You went for a stew with the name "Alexander the Great's Irritable Bleeding Nipples." This contained Turkish *sucuk* sausage tossed with finely sliced celery, chipotle and chopped tomatoes lightly sautéed in a pan. On the side, you served hulled barley cooked in Aquavit. In my intoxication, I considered simply laying down to die as you set a standard that seemed almost impossible to breach. But a new day brought with it new energy in the kitchen. I surprised myself with the dish "Swedenborg's Windowsill." Potatoes, cabbage, fennel and sliced pineapple stewed in their own juices for some hours and then pureed. While that was settling, I removed the vacuum packed beef filet that had been marinating in a sous vide for 32 hours at 52 degrees celsius. Cutting open the vacuum bag, I dumped the contents out onto our plates and served the mush next to it. A few sprinkles of peppercorns and our food was ready. Enchanted by our poetic cuisine, we decided to publish a cookbook. Naturally, we viewed this endeavour as a continuation of our black signs project, an extension of the overall task—the time spent on our cookbook was thereby justified. You wanted to make a cookbook of poetic dishes, but if we didn't want to publish with a pay-and-print publisher from the U.S., we would have to come up with some other concept. During a brainstorming session, we came up with the idea to make a cookbook with favourite meals of the world's dictators. In the richly illustrated book, "Dictators' Favourites", one could find an exquisite *vitello tonato* recipe from Mussolini's grandmother and his original Sicilian fennel salad with mandarin juice and warm pine nuts. Other obvious favourites were Robert Mugabe's spicy chicken jerky and the Gadaffi family's enchanting sour lamb tagine. In the winter, our steadfast readers could warm themselves with Josef Stalin's semolina porridge with warm gooseberry jam or a steaming bowl of Pol Pot's Pho Bò soup. If one had to work overtime, Pinochet's mustard-based cheese sandwich was a favourite among young people, since it was easy to make by oneself. Not surprisingly, the book was accepted by a large publishing house after a quick round of bids. Everyone found it so hilarious to prepare "Quisling's Cod" or "Hussein's Hamburger" for their loved ones, and thereby cultivate an ironic gastronomic relationship to the world's dictators. The book sold so well that we followed it up with a volume on meals from well known white-collar criminals and traitors. After the royalty checks started pouring into our postbox, we thought for a moment that this might be the source we needed to fund production of the signs. Slowly but surely, however, we realized that this was an illusion. Although the royalty amounts reached five digits, approaching six, we would need far more money than the cookbook could give us. Colossal sums were required to produce 52 million signs. As the publishing payments decreased with each quarter, and when the editors said no to a collection of recipes from popular terrorists and sex offenders, we abandoned the publishing sector as quickly as we had joined it. Keeping in mind the rapid generation of black signs, which seemed to be endless, we perceived the only solution. Grandma would have to call it a night and then we would be able to inherit her world famous jutegnask collection. It was here that we would find the wealth needed to realise our plan.

The woman was 107 years old. We decided to wait it out.

Dear Gustimoldo

Good days don't last forever. There is a limit to how many black signs a soul can bear before it snaps. The day before you disappeared, we were out celebrating our anticipated financial inheritance. In the gentlemen's bathroom, I stood in front of the mirror snapping my fingers above my head as I combed the two last hairs into place, and was suddenly embarrassed to notice two men standing behind me. I was up for anything. On our table out in the pub, your beer had been left alone. I took it for granted that you had left to hold one of your urban sermons but I couldn't find you at any of your usual podiums at Youngstorget, Torggaten or Markveien. As I walked back, disappointed, to get our jackets, I heard a voice from under the Eventyrbrua bridge. I crept down the slope toward the river and saw you standing there, utterly alone beneath the bridge about to launch into one of your sermons. But something was amiss. In contrast to all of your other sermons, there was no audience, not even beggars or drug pushers. Were you ashamed of what you were planning to say? You turned over a trash bin and placed one foot upon it in your familiar stance. But everything else seemed out of place. You coughed and rubbed your chin, couldn't seem to get your gears going. You began orating on an inhalation, half choking yourself, as if the signal between your head and mouth had faltered. On top of this, you moved your hands in gestures to underscore words that weren't coming out. I pressed my body tightly against the stone wall, scared to death that you would notice my presence. You loosened up a bit and the words began to flow. Following those initial difficulties, you went on to deliver one of the most painful sermons I have ever been witness to. You screamed out five lines to a refrain.

I am weary of our so-called task.
I have lost faith in our purpose.
We are meaningless, vile, absurd.
We have lost all relevance.
We are wretched.

The bridge was like a chamber of echoes and your words ricocheted off the walls. The arched stonewalls functioned not only as a storage space for the reverberating words, but as an instrument in itself. The words blended and intersected with each other, bathing the vaulted structure in sound. The signal increased in volume and was broadcasted out to Oslo.

Wretched. Relevance. Lost. Task.

As I listed to the matchless music machine of the Eventyrbrua bridge, I saw your smile edging onto your lips. Did you realize that we were just as wretched as everyone else, only that we had screamed out "Let there be darkness!"? Or was it that you foresaw the consequences of the black signs and were thereby able to turn away from an obsession, a misstep? Was there, somewhere deep inside of you, another person who never emerged from behind that distorted face, that snickering laughter, that howl, that path that you had gotten yourself onto? No, you will not be allowed that honour. You smiled beneath the bridge because you had discovered another project in which to invest your energies, another task by which you could draw others in and leave them hanging, as you did with me.

Gustimoldo—the eternal agitator.

A usurer in hate.

In remorse of the dream.

I am weary of our so-called task.
I have lost faith in our purpose.
We are meaningless, vile, absurd.
We have lost all relevance.
We are wretched.

I couldn't stand to hear any more.

Your name will be remembered in a cough of a dog.

The day after your sermon, you drove to an industrial area at Økern to inspect two sign suppliers. By accident, you walked straight into a hall that produced strips, those plastic cable ties with locks that everyone from carpenters to institutions use. At the end of the hall, you noticed an assembly line on which a machine spit out thousands of cable ties at once. An eager sales consultant came over and handed you a brochure containing six different cable tie samples in various thicknesses, lengths and colours. You thumbed through to a page informing you that the most common 18 cm long model cost 0.5 cents per piece on an order between one and 5,000 pieces. For a larger order of up to 10,000 ties, the price was reduced to 0.425 cents. Any order over 10,000 was priced at 0.375 cents. I knew about your fear of cable ties, Gustimoldo. You had decided that this little strip of plastic was the worst of human inventions. It was a symbol of oppression and of our active engagement towards it. This oblong, thin strip demonstrated how lost we were, how little character we truly possessed, how deeply into our isolation we had burrowed. In this small factory hall in Oslo, enough cable ties were produced to keep half of the world in chains. You walked over to the assembly line and felt with the tip of your finger the long strips of plastic that passed by. The seller later told me that you then sank down, lay on your side and curled into a ball. You had to abandon the jutegnask, the black signs, and continue on your swim.

You sent me postcards for half a year from all the corners of the world.

And then you stopped.

I must write the black history alone.

LEFT OVER CAVIAR FROM SVERRE AND INGRID FEHN'S MIDSUMMER'S EVE PARTY ON HVASSER (1976)

While Arne Nordheim, Sverre Fehn, Ingrid Fehn and Rannveig Getz were busy trying to toss Inger Sitter into the water as a result of a lost bet, Grandma scraped some caviar from their plates and put it into a disinfected mason jar.

Mason jar containing caviar residue
G- (turned to dust)
JG982829

SIGNED FIRST EDITION OF ORNETTE COLEMAN'S SHAPE OF JAZZ TO COME (1966)

An inscription on the inner sleeve says: "To my lonely woman, Ornette."

Vinyl and cardboard
NM
JG982830

PHOTOGRAPH OF GRANDMA, ORSON WELLES AND OJA KODAR (1972)

Taken with a self-timer during their road trip around Spain in Grandma's old Saab on the search for locations for Welle's film project about Don Quixote.

Black and white photograph
G+
JG982831

IVER JÅK'S COPY OF NILS-ASLAK VALKEPÄÄS' LÁVLLO VIZÁR BIELLOCIZÁS (1978)

Originating from when Grandma travelled to Kautokeino to offer moral support to eight young Sami artists who wished to found the artist collective MASI. Following her visit, Grandma stayed with her good friend Iver Jåks at the Vardø lighthouse for a week, where they were tasked with performing intricate rituals to drive out demons left over from the German occupation. The dedication on the flap reads: "You are everything to me. The yearning behind yearning itself. Iver."

Paper, bound
G- (one page of the poetry collection is missing, torn out)
JG982832

JOHNNY DEPP'S TOBACCO PIPE (1991)

Ivory pipe that was given to Grandma for introducing Depp to Hunter S. Thompson at the Elephant Rifle Congress in Nevada in 1991.

Ivory, metal, tobacco
NM
JG982833

BURLAP SACK FROM THE SURREALIST EXHIBITION AT THE GALÉRIE BEAUX ARTS PARIS (1938)

Grandma is said to have singlehandedly persuaded the museum director of the Galéri Beaux Arts to allow the group of surrealists to use taped field recordings of screams from mental patients and the smell of coffee as a part of the exhibition design. As the show was being dismantled at the end, Grandma snatched several burlap sacks and old coffee filters.

Hemp and cotton fibres
NM
JG982834

"DERRIÈRE LE MIROIR N° 210" (1974)

Grandma was presented with this first edition by Georges Raillard after a late lunch on the seafront promenade in Nice. On the inside flap, a written note says: "Dearest, here is a little text I've written on Tapies. It's no longer something for me, but I know that you are drawn to his monotopies."

Arches paper
VG+
JG982835

WORLD CLASS WRECKIN CRU'S RAPPED IN ROMANCE LP (1986)
Andrew Young, later known as Dr. Dre, has signed the cover with: "Thanks for bringing out my feminine side, my panther from the North Sea's burning ocean."

Vinyl, cardboard cover
VG+
JG982836

MARGOT FONTEYN'S LILY NOSEGAY (1961)
A nosegay of lilies from Margot Fonteyn, thanking Grandma for having brought Rudolf Nureyev to reason backstage, which resulted in his withdrawal from the Kirov ballet's tour during their stop in Paris.

Lilies and paper
VG+ (shrivelled)
JG982837

LEV TERMEN'S SMASHED THEREMIN (1919)
A destroyed copy of the first theremin ever to be produced. Delivered to the doorstep as a clear message to Grandma from Lev Termen (later Léon Theremin) after she dumped him in favour of Mayakovsky. A note from Termen reads: "'I fix the sun like a monocle into my gaping eye'" – whatever that means – and you swapped me for that ass."

Copper
G- (smashed and irreparable)
JG982836

PIECE OF HERBERT VON KARAJAN'S TOOTH (1976)

From the time that Grandma and Karajan ate a Strammer Max sandwich at the Markthalle Kreuzberg with a journalist from *Der Spiegel*. When the journalist slipped the question of Karajan's thoughts about the Berlin Symphony's transition into the "Reich Orchestra" under the Nazis, Herbert clenched his teeth so hard that he chipped off a piece and then dashed to the toilet. Grandma extracted the bit of tooth from the dark bread slice and placed it into her wallet.

Piece of tooth
VG (coffee stains)
JG982839

HARALD GRIEG'S HOME BREWED RED WINE (1967)

In 1942, Grandma turned up at Grieg's office claiming that Tore Hamsun gave her his wine kegs, sacks of yeast and remaining stocks of alcohol. Grandma kept seven bottles of red wine for herself. The wine has soured, but works well as red wine vinegar for fresh dressings or to sweeten artichoke and trumpet mushroom soups.

Green glass bottle
G+ (wine/vinegar)
JG982840

PHOTOGRAPH OF GRANDMA, DAVID BOWIE, BERNARD PURDIE, JAKI LIEBEZEIT AND BRIAN ENO AT THE FELA KUTI-CONCERT AT ROUNDHOUSE IN LONDON (1970)

A photograph of Grandma and the gang that she gathered for fun around Kuti's concert. Everyone is wearing a t-shirt that she had printed and distributed before the show. Across the chest is written "Tony Allen Fan Club."

Black and white photograph
VG-
JG982841

CLEMENT GREENBERG'S DOCUMENTARY VIDEO (1972)

An amateur video recording showing Grandma and Greenberg in conversation about Edvard Munch and his relationship to Japanese wood block prints. In the second half, they discuss the relationship between the use of perspective and shadowing used by Giotto and Egyptian grave painters. Toward the end of the footage, Greenberg makes a joke directed against Meyer Schapiro. The joke is very vulgar and is about a person who calls the police regarding a flasher, and the policeman asks the caller to prove it over the phone. The video ends on a note of subdued, polite laughter.

JVC120 Video Cassette
VG+
JG982842

PHOTO OF GRANDMA, FRANTZ FANON AND JEAN-PAUL SARTRE (1961)

Photo taken with a self-timer in which Grandma and Sartre are posing in front of Fanon's hospital bed in Moscow. Fanon is holding up a copy of the newly published *Les damnés de la terre* with a sad smile on his mouth.

Black and white photograph
VG
JG982843

LIGHT BULB FROM ATSUKO TANAKA'S ELECTRIC DRESS (1957)

During a trip to Japan in 1956, Grandma introduced Tanaka to Akira Kanayama, and by extension, to the Gutai group. Tanaka was eternally grateful and always invited Grandma to stay for free in her studio. Grandma took this opportunity to unscrew one light bulb from *Electric Dress*.

40 watt Osram light bulb
VG+
JG982844

ELISABETH GRANNEMAN OR JOHAN BORGEN'S TOUPEE (1966)

Two notes from Grandma indicate the object's possible origins. The first states that the toupee may be from the time that the young debutant ripped off Granneman's toupee at Theatrecaféen and took it with her as a trophy to Gyldendal publishing house's spring launch at the Art House. The other note hints that Grandma was present when Johan Borgen used his advance payment from *The Red Mist* to restore his hair loss after being suckered by an advertisement in the *Dagbladet* newspaper. Upon viewing himself in the mirror, Borgen realized how idiotic he looked and resolutely threw the toupee into the trash bin. Of course, Grandma took it back out for safekeeping.

Toupee from Ruh's Hairstudio
M (unused)
JG982845

FEDERICO FELLINI'S HOMEMADE PAGLIATA (1972)

As Fellini struggled to come up with the final scene to his film *Roma*, Grandma suggested that he film several young people driving motorcycles and Vespas through the streets of Rome by night. Fellini was ecstatic at her suggestion and cooked up his homemade pagliata for Grandma and Nino Rota to celebrate that the final scene of the film was now set.

Calf intestines
G- (decayed)
JG982846

Dear Gustimoldo

The black signs are being delivered more and more frequently now, and I am in sore need of your help. Some of the truck drivers don't even speak English and, if I had to guess, come all the way from North China or East Africa. The capacity of our regular sign printer has been fully overloaded, so I have had to commission suppliers from all over the world. Using exaggerated gestures, I signal with body language to the drivers that they should head up the gravel lane and unload the signs inside the garden, and for god's sake not to offload them in front of the gateway or dump the palettes on the main road. I signal to them to keep quiet, turn off their radios and not to keep their vehicles idling. Then I struggle alone throughout the night to manoeuvre the pallets of signs up the ramp before the neighbours get suspicious.

Yesterday, a grey Mercedes with a private chauffeur came driving up to the house. At first I thought it was one of the ambassadorial neighbours come to complain, but out stepped a tall Eastern European man who introduced himself as the owner of a sign factory. He was on errand in Oslo to present me with a gold wristwatch and to thank the factory's unquestionably best client. The confidence that we bestowed in them meant so much for him and his workers. He fastened the watch to my wrist and I could see that he was taken aback when he realized where all of the signs had ended up. Still, he invited me and my non-existent wife to dinner at one of Oslo's best restaurants. I thanked him and declined. Another challenge that we must discuss, now that we are on the topic, is that the house is going to buckle soon under the weight of all the signs. The attic and second floor are laden with black signs and the structure is top-heavy. It bends with the slightest breeze which is causing extensive damage to both the brick facade and the roof. One possible solution is to construct supporting vertical columns from stacked signs in certain strategic points on the first floor. That way, even if the centuries-old support beams should give way from the weight, the columns would, hopefully, continue to uphold the house.

Our fib about the house renovations is beginning to show some serious cracks.

Dear Gustimoldo

This morning I awoke to a cacophony of gibberish. More than fifteen trucks stood idling in a line outside of the house and the drivers were engaged in full-on fist fights. Our logistics are blown. After announcing that I was the responsible project leader and safety manager, I was able to calm some tempers and coordinate everything to get the signs unloaded in the garden, truckload after truckload. There are now 591 stacked pallets the size of two medium sized Norwegian mountain cabins in the garden. I am in for a long night.

Hard work serves to curb feelings of anxiety.

Gustimoldo, I am not going to judge myself. I am tired yet happy that we are so close to fulfilling our task. The black signs continue to be produced and soon all of the jutegnask will be auctioned off—who would have believed we two could achieve so much? Yet, in the depths of my soul, a clump of unrelenting awareness is growing, pressing its way upward: you are never coming home, and we will never hang up the black signs.

Gustimoldo, if you are out there:

Come home.
Come forth.

I am asking you now.

Dear Gustimoldo

The auctions are going triumphantly, and I can say with muted enthusiasm: the milk spurts from Grandma. You would not believe the price that Wolf Vostell's bloody toothpick raised when the gavel swung for the third time. An insurance policy signed by Charles Ives raked in close to $2,000, while a bronze samovar—a gift from Rachmaninoff to Grandma in thanks for translating his letter to Arnold Schönberg—seemed to be caught in an endlessly escalating bidding war. Yesterday, Kurt Cobain's cigarette stub, which he smoked and stamped out backstage at an Earth concert in 1989, went for over $4,000. The lucky purchaser was a teenager from Dalarna in Sweden who emptied his savings account of all the money he'd received for his confirmation. In plain, simple words, Gustimoldo—we now have an influx of funds at our disposal that we never could have anticipated.

It obliges us to our task.

I have calculated that the amount of black signs which we can produce for these sums of money are out of proportion. Just listen, Gustimoldo. Kurt Schwitter's rusty nail clippers were sold for $26,000 to a collector from Switzerland. A museum for literature in the U.S.A. coughed up $37,000 for Grandma's kitchen table. Their representatives were, of course, only interested in Ezra Pound's bite marks along the right table leg, which originated during an erotic table game that Grandma and Pound made up over a bottle of Cointreau. Sergej Eisenstein's fly fishing gear, which contained six flies tied by Eisenstein himself, went under the auctioneer hammer for over $15,000 dollars last week. A stick of eyeliner that Grandma pinched from Jacques Prévert during the filming of *Les Enfants Du Paradis* brought in $1,500. Can you recall that gruesome photograph of Grandma and Jaco Pastorius, who are laying on a nudist beach at the Baltic Sea in red leather shorts while downing white russians? A purchaser from Russia paid $8,000 to be able to add this to his collection of Pastorius jutegnask. Just the other day, I began going through the trays that we have full of invitations, letters and seasonal and birthday greetings cards, which have been safely stored in eight trunks in the cellar. Among these, I caught a glimpse of correspondences with people like Charlie Chaplin, Tom Sandberg, Walter Gibbons, Ulrike Ottinger, Tobias Rehberger, Thomas Bernhard, Luigi Nono, Delia Derbyshire, the OHO Group, Kool Herc, Bonnie Dobson, Maya Deren and Alexander Hammid, Inger Sitter, Lloyd Kaufman, Quentin Meillassoux, Adrian Henri, Leni Riefenstahl, Jenny Hval, Lawrence Weiner, Frank Sinatra, Luc Tuymans, Max Frisch, Kjell Bækkelund, Rudolf Steinner, Thurston Moore and Kim Gordon, Stan Vanderbeek, Jack Nitzsche, Wilhelm Reich, Joseph Kosuth, Roy Harper, Ed Kienholz, Ferdinand de Saussure, Hans Richter, Otto Dix, Henri Bergson, Issey Miyake, Mary Ellen Bute, Barbet Schroeder, Francis Alÿs, Stein Mehren, Wong Kar-Wai, Jeff Mills, Lydia Lunch, Otto Piene, Anton Webern, Jasper Johns, Carolyn Christov-Bakargiev, Linda Perhacs, Pierre Alechinsky and Ferry Radax. I put some of them into plastic bags and listed them on the auction site. It brought in $50,000. I wonder whether we should sell this material by weight—would it be by kilo or by half-kilo of "Grandma's Mail"? Do you get my point? The craving for jutegnask is larger than we anticipated; people are willing to pay almost anything. A doggy bag with leftover broccoli spätzle, that Richard Wagner's widow Cosima served Grandma in Bayreuth in 1919, sold for $18,000 to a Polish

Wagner fanatic. A few hours after the close of the auction, I received a note from a U.S. trader who was willing to double the selling price if I would cancel the sale with the Pole. He had been in an airplane when the auction ended and seemed quite desperate to somehow acquire the Wagner spätzle for his collection. Do you remember Gus van Sant's striped pyjamas, the ones that looked like a prison uniform? Those sold for $2,000 yesterday. A love poem entitled "Ta ma Ladi, wy did u liive me in da rain?" written by Linton Kwesi Johnson to Grandma, was auctioned off for $5,800. More than twice a single month's salary. Enough for over a hundred signs.

This unexpected amount of wealth has led to a few changes. Our original work on the black signs has been produced and delivered in full. The challenge is that there are still boxes full of jutegnask in the cellar and the money in the account is far from spent. There is really only a single solution, Gustimoldo—the sign generator must be switched on again. There is one minor problem with this. Our black history was complete and final, so where, exactly, should I find new material for spreading blame? I cannot begin working on creating new signs by myself, nor can I start going through all of our file cabinets to check if there wasn't something we may have missed. There is only a single solution, Gustimoldo—I must start printing signs for dark histories that might happen in the future. Before you laugh or open your mouth in protest, just listen: we can be relatively certain that the next 100 years are going to be filled with just as much blame and wretchedness, if not even more, than the past has been. Although affluence is increasing worldwide, the complaints will simply become more frequent and pointed. It is to the future that we must now turn our focus, Gustimoldo, it is here that the blame lies. The bile and rancour of the future will be distributed at some point, so why not beforehand? Look at some of the suggestions that the sign generator came up with:

EBBA MARIE ASPERUD (2509–2589)

Ebba Marie Asperud left her husband after he tried to strangle her in front of their two children. Asperud reported her husband's offence while at the ER and her husband was convicted of aggravated assault in the presence of children. Following this incident, she remained single, marked by the loss of her best friend, husband, the father of her children, and her abuser.

KENNETH ALMEN (2688–2751)

During Almen's thirtieth birthday, certain unknown thieves decided to steal all of the guests' shoes that were lined up in the stairwell. The mood of the party was considerably dampened when the theft was discovered, and all of the guests had to take taxis home in the snowy weather.

MAME DIANGO (3711–3799)

Was labelled "coloured" by a regular at the local pub, only to be thrown out when he challenged the man. When he returned to the pub with the police to report the crime, there was no one among the regular gang of drinkers—whom he took as resigned alcoholics but nonetheless honest Norwegians—who would support his version of the story.

ELIN LIE-HANSEN (7129–7203)

Started a popular blog that followed her personal struggle against lymphoma. After her recovery from the cancer, few people followed her blog anymore. Elin developed significant self-esteem issues due to the decrease in hits on her page and began to wish that the cancer would return in one form or another.

What do you think? It is uncertain, speculative and crammed full of dumbfounding anachronisms, but I think it is acceptable. The future's black history is endless; let us be the first to write it. Just wait—if you don't come home soon, I will have to start writing the black history of animals and birchwoods too.

Dear Gustimoldo

The signs can no longer be trusted. Yesterday, I stacked signs in the cellar and constructed a passageway that ended at the stairwell. While I was working in the innermost room in the cellar, the signs moved behind my back and closed me in. My only salvation from a long and painful death was a small, sunken tunnel at the top where the passage had once been. There was barely enough room for a body, and I squirmed my way forward with the help of my elbows. My stomach and chest were slowly sliced up and my back was clawed at by the ceiling. As I neared the stairs, I was sure that the signs were playing a trick on me, that they would torture me, scrape me off and drive in a stake. When I finally got there, I fell out of the tunnel headfirst. I had so little strength left in my arms that I wasn't able to soften my fall. My chin hit the floor. I woke again in a pool of blood and found my entire body cut to shreds. I managed to pull myself up to the bedroom, where I wrapped my limbs in several white sheets. It seems that the bleeding has stopped for now. I am sitting on the edge of the bed, in a beam of tender morning light. I look like a pitiful Greek.

The signs no longer need me. They are trying to rid me from the house.

The signs are impatient.

Dear Gustimoldo

The house is nearing its saturation point. I have managed to carve out for myself a small hovel in the library from the space that remains. A mattress, technical equipment, yoghurt and a desk are all that I can squeeze in; the signs have taken over the rest of the room. The bathroom is no longer attainable, so I use a hose for my hygienic rituals and go to the garden to do my duty. Oslo winter has descended on the city and you can imagine how frigid my morning showers are now. Aside from placing orders for future black signs, thereby emptying our bank account, my only pastime now is to practice hanging up signs. At the far end of the room, I have jerry-rigged a small private test facility so that I can try out various surfaces and equipment for the most efficient methods of suspension. My personal record for hanging a black sign on a concrete surface is 34.2 seconds. I can get it down to about 30 seconds if the sign is being hung on metal. Each sign has four mounting points and just as many screws. With hard work and exercise, I am hoping to get my times down to 30 and 20 seconds, respectively. A half a minute is still an eternity if one is mounting signs in downtown Oslo but this is the quickest possible option. Hanging up signs certainly promises to be a risky operation.

Even dwarves have to start small.

One issue, which is much more problematic, is the noise. We have got to discuss this, Gustimoldo. Hanging up the signs causes a terrible racket. I already mentioned that the problem might be solved with a muffler or a capsule, but I have not been able to locate a suitable engineer who is willing to take on the task. It appears that a muffler would make the drill very heavy, and this would lead to other challenges. We also need to look into other methods for mounting the signs on glass and marble surfaces. A drill does not work in these cases, and glue and traditional adhesives are much too easy to peel off. Perhaps the old hooligan trick—glue mixed with crushed glass—is our best option?

Enough details.

What I actually wanted to tell you, which is the most important thing, is that the feeling of putting up a sign is something momentous. From the placement and the drilling, that moment when you take a step backwards, lift up the safety goggles and observe the sign that has been attached and hung—it tugs at the heartstrings.

A black sign hung up is a powerful sight to behold.

Dear Gustimoldo

There is an image that comes to mind when I think of you. It is from a comedy series. A bunch of school kids and their teacher sit at a bus stop. Suddenly a kid named John runs into the street and gets violently run over by a bus. Blood and bowelguts fly up into the air everywhere. The teacher cries out: "Call John an ambulance! Call John an ambulance!" The kids just screams and laugh: "John is an ambulance! John is an ambulance!"

Dear Gustimoldo,

The doorbell rang. Since I didn't hear any large trucks unloading pallets or Creole dialects, I realized that something else awaited me at the door. Was it you, there to embrace me with a cartload of apologies? I was prepared to forgive you everything: your disappearance, the anguish, the fear you put me through. Had you finally come to understand that we belonged together, that we filled one another with purpose, and that there wasn't anything to fear? It rang again. The guest held their finger on the doorbell for a long while. I looked out through the peephole. It wasn't you standing there, but Grandma with two leather bags in her hand.

> *Sorry that I'm so late. I have been at Öland getting a*
> *doctorate in glass blowing.*

I opened the door a crack and she shoved it all the way open, wrapping me in a hug as an apology for her long absence. Her skin was different than it had been at the nursing home. Her lips were now full and warm, not cracked and covered in sores. The last time she had kissed me, it had been like a dry leaf pressed against my cheek, but now a small circle of saliva was left on my face. It wasn't the same person who now stood before me, and who I had buried at Our Saviour's Cemetery. This was another Grandma. She asked me to take her bags up to her room while she untied the laces on her winter boots with one hand and removed her hairpin with the other. Her long black hair tumbled down across her back. There wasn't a single grey hair. I mustered a brave smile, clutched her bags and bounded up the stairs. In a panic I tossed the bags into a corner of the bedroom and scurried into the bathroom. Why had I run upstairs where it was impossible to sneak away? In a confusion of anxiety and guilt, I crouched in the space between the tub and toilet and placed some signs on top to cover me. The only thing I could think about was the cry that would soon break out and the hurried steps that would draw near to my hiding place.

After an hour, I crawled out again. I had realized that there was nothing for it but to go down and confess to Grandma about what we had done in her absence. I descended the stairs slowly and slipped into the kitchen. Grandma was sitting there in her indoor turban and sarong, designed by Johannes Itten, as though nothing at all had happened. She sipped at her afternoon drink, vodka with citrus. Spread out across a provisional table fashioned from black signs, she was playing chess with herself on a pocket chess board that she'd stolen from John Cage. In between moves, she leafed through a book about Goethe's theory of colours.

She must have understood, Gustimoldo. The entire kitchen was crammed full of black signs, and there wasn't a single item of jutegnask in sight. Yet despite all of this, she appeared calm and mild as I entered the room. Perhaps I should have said something to her, apologized for our actions, but it seemed futile. I was never able to talk to Grandma about my feelings or desires. Not because she didn't take me seriously, mind you, but because she would always expand it and make it a part of her own universe. She would aestheticise it, theorize it and refashion the inner workings of my soul into political-cultural issues. She would take it away from me. When she noticed that I had come in, she looked up from Goethe's theory of colours. In her passive-aggressive tone, the one that made "change the light bulb" sound like a twelve-hour-long birthing contraction, she said:

It was not nice of you to get rid of Ingmar Bergman's post-it notes that were hanging on the fridge. One of

them had a recipe for rye cracker bread that I was
thinking of baking soon. Ingo had such a flair for
baking cracker bread, you know, he was simply un-
surpassable.

That was all she said. Full stop. Gustimoldo—I believe she was relieved that the jutegnask was gone, that she in fact looked forward to begin a new collection, or that she was happy that I had finally shown a will to act. After a long sip, she took out one of Goethe's coloured spinning tops. It spun around on the table and she gazed intently at the basic colours as they blended into each other. I am now completely certain. Grandma was not a person. She was an indescribable force that has wandered restlessly throughout the earth's continents since the dawn of time, collecting jutegnask. Always ahead. The direction mattered little, what mattered was that it was always ahead. As I watched her sitting there alone, wondering at the top like a small child, I understood that creation can engender as much distance as destruction. She would always be alone, a shadow of a person. When Goethe's spinning top at last foundered onto its side, she looked up and asked me: "Is there anything going on tonight, some grand opening or festivities?" She was 108 years old.

I awoke with a warm pain across my temple. Grandma was no longer there. My headache refused to go away even after a frigid shower beneath the garden hose. When I put myself to bed for the evening, I looked up at the columns of signs looming high above me in the library. In the dim light, they appeared like a black broom, ready to sweep me away.

I'm certain of this.

The black signs want me out of the house so that they can be hung up.

Dear Gustimoldo

The house is full. I removed the radiators, yanked up the parquet and tore out the sewage pipes to cram the last signs in. They only barely fit. I had to stack 200 signs in the chimney, so it is ice cold now that the fireplace is no longer in service. The structure of the building is under so much duress that I dare not remove a single nail for fear that the house will collapse. Maybe that wouldn't be such a bad idea. The signs would form a tidal wave out of the house and slide down the icy hills toward the city. The January winds would assist in forming a crossfire of signs that would be impossible to avoid.

Oslo buried alive.

The last auction ends in seven days. Gustimoldo—it isn't just any piece of jutegnask that I have put up for sale this time. Besides those things stored in the cellar, this auction includes the most extraordinary object in Grandma's jutegnask collection, the central boiling system, one could say, of the entire operation. Within the rose-painted chest from South Gudbrandsdal—which she received as a gift from Alf Prøysen after having persuaded him to make Gunvor Smikkstugun a hero in his novel *Trost i taklampa*—she stored jutegnask items of the greatest sentimental value. The chest holds Ernst Ludwig Kirchner's zebra-striped bathrobe, the one she was given when she was only four years old. It really smells like man. Upon further reflection, one may decide that Kirchner can be forgiven. Beneath this is the blanket in which Louise Bourgeois swaddled me, complete with blood and dried placenta, that's how fresh I was when they came to fetch me in Finnmark. One can clearly see that Bourgeois, out of sheer boredom

and most likely somewhere around the vicinity of Trondheim, began shaping the blanket and its contained juices
into a little sculpture. I believe that this sculpture, if one
can call it such, will sell for millions. Under the blanket
is a history book about pickled herring and cured hákarl.
Grandma received this tome from Robert Mapplethorpe,
who noticed how unhappily in love she was with the dentist and wished to help her gain entry to his affections. The
strange thing, Gustimoldo, is that you and I are also represented in this treasure chest. There is a framed photo inside, of us on a trip to the Tivoli fun park with Grandma,
Bjørn Winsnes and Hans Hammarskjöld, our trip was
connected to Tiofoto's 30th birthday party in Göteborg.
Do you remember how we found that old man at Liseberg
who had cut out the faces from large film posters so that
you could stick your face in and pose for a photo? I posed
as Conan the Barbarian and you as a Blues Brother, and
Hammarskjöld snapped a passing shot. I had to wash my
hands thoroughly with warm water and soap after seeing
what lay beneath the picture frame in the chest. Within a
silver-plated jewellery box, the remains of Picasso's burst
condom had been placed, both ends having been tied off
with fishing twine. The rubber had long since dissolved to
powder and only the twine was left, but that hadn't kept
Grandma from sparing any details in describing the object
in an accompanying note. She had tried all of the fertility tricks in the book in order to bear Picasso's child, to no
avail. Yet her firm belief in the advances of science led her
to hold on to this relic. The last item in Grandma's wooden
chest does not fall under the category of jutegnask, but I
will tell you what it is anyway. At the very bottom of the
chest is the painting that Grandma showed at her Academy graduate exhibition in 1921. The motif is this house.
It has been painted in soft pastels and portrays a house of

joy. The garden is bursting with fruit, children and adults frolic in a ring—the house glows with upright kindness. It is a piece by a Sunday painter, worth less than an old sack of potatoes. I hold Grandma's painting up toward the light and take a look at my surroundings. I can see no resemblance. The house is on the verge of collapse and dark. It bears an unpleasant odour and there isn't anything like the garden of Eden from out beyond the veranda door. On the contrary. The house is marked by the seriousness of its time. The painting is going straight into the rubbish, it's the only thing in the house that I will throw away.

Gustimoldo, in case you haven't returned by the time the last auction is over, the writing of the history of the black signs may now be considered finished.

HANS JØRGEN TOMING'S LENTICULAR OBJECT (1969)

Inspired by the Julio le Parc exhibition at the Henie Onstad Kunstsenter, Tomming produced a lenticular object that shows his wife Lisbeth in the process of taking a photo. Seen from one angle, she is holding the camera down at her side in a resting pose. When tilted to the side, the lenticular object shows that his wife has lifted the camera and is in position.

Lenticular object
M- (like new)
JG7912393

PHOTOGRAPH OF ALBERTO GIACOMETTI AND GRANDMA (1959)

Taken with a self-timer at the Staatliche Kunsthalle in Karlsruhe, Germany. The duo is posing in front of Albrecht Dürer's copper plate "Melencholia I". Alberto is pointing at the copper plate's 12-sided polyhedron while giving a thumbs-up to the camera.

Black and white photograph
VG
JG7912394

LETTER FROM ORSON WELLES AND OJA KODAR (1974)

They write that they miss Grandma deeply and that they have located a place in Morocco called Essaouira. Orson is dead certain that he is going to use the location to film his next project on MacBeth: "Come! Come! Come! We'll go visit Bowles in Marrakesh afterwards!" the letter concludes.

Paper
VG+
JG7912395

EGYPTIAN LOVERS' SWEATY WRISTBAND (1981)

Grandma and Egyptian Lover attended the Uncle Jamm's Army dance festival at the Santa Monica Convention Centre on Christmas Eve in 1981. During a provocative hip-to-hip dance manoeuvre, Grandma managed to grab the wristband from his arm and shove it down into her panties. She stored it there until the following day, along with other objects that she had picked up during the night, including Rodger Clayton's seven-inch of Dr. John's "Right Place, Wrong Time". Writing on the wristband reads: "Sexy, ain't it?"

Cotton
VG
JG7912396

JOYCE CAROL OATES' ATROPINE BOTTLE (1989)

Grandma had to take a trip to the pharmacy at the railway station to buy both atropine and spersadex when the iritis in Oates' eye developed quickly during her visit to Oslo in 1989. She kept the atropine bottle in return for her efforts.

Amber coloured glass
VG- (empty)
JG7912397

PAN CRIOLLO PAMPHLET BY XUL SOLAR (1950)

An inscription on the back written by Solar and Emilio Pettoruti, thanking Grandma for helping them to locate a spacious studio for rent in the Palermo district. In his own language, Pan Criollo, Solar has written: "My beloved, I shall invent a new chess game for you. Xul."

Hardcover, uncoated paper
VG
JG7912398

JEAN GENET'S BATH TOWEL (1983)

After Grandma sent the novel *Querelle de Brest* to Fassbinder and arranged for Brad Davis and Jeanne Moreau to accept roles in the film, Genet invited her to his house in Larache, Morocco. Grandma took this opportunity to steal a towel with the initials "H.V.P." from Genet's guest bathroom, which he had originally stolen from the Hotel De Ville Paris.

Terrycloth towel
G+ (well used)
JG7912399

EL LISITSKIJ'S SHEEPSKIN THROW (1922)

Originating from a Russian variation of the Norwegian short-tailed sheep. A note written on the backside of the throw says: "Thank you for helping me and Dorner to refine the idea of making the rooms in the Landesmuseum Hannover more atmospheric. You are a gem! El."

Sheepskin
VG
JG7912400

ROOTS MANUVA'S BUSINESS CARD (2002)

Grandma helped Rodney to clear the Bernard Parmegiani sample that he used in his song "Witness", since she was a close friend of the composer. Roots Manuva heard a snippet of the song by chance in the Charles de Gaulle airport on his way home from playing in Paris. Grandma arranged everything from getting the original tracks to clearing the rights.

Paper
VG+
JG7912401

KIRSTEN FLAGSTAD'S VIKING HELMET (1947)

An inscription on the side of the helmet has been written in black pen: "Dearest. The Wagerians in New York are suffocating me with their admiration. Maybe I'll never play anything else but a Viking dame with a spear in hand. I now have thousands of Viking helmets in my closet. Dearest, now you have one too."

Plastic
NM
JG7912402

HILDEGARD KNEF'S WIENERSCHNITZEL (1964)

From a dinner at the restaurant Max und Frisch at Moritzplatz in Berlin, where Grandma convinced Hildegard to make an entire LP with Kurt Tucholsky's texts. When Hildegard didn't finish the rest of her schnitzel, Grandma asked the waiter to put it in a doggy bag, although she wasn't the least bit hungry.

Pork
G- (rotten)
JG7912403

WERNER HERZOG'S VIDEOCASSETTE (1979)

Cassette with raw material from Herzog's first recording of *Fitzcarraldo* in 1979. The tape shows Jason Robards and Mick Jagger eating grilled chicken on the riverbank while Grandma and Herzog frantically engage in negotiations with the head of a local native tribe in the background.

Panasonic VHS
VG+
JG7912404

PHOTOGRAPH OF GRANDMA, ERICH MARX, KATHARINA SIEVERDING AND JOSEF PAUL KLEIHUES (1996)

Snapped at the opening of the Hamburger Bahnhof, Berlin, by a journalist from the *Berliner Zeitung*. A cheerful mood, except for Katharina Sieverding, who is glaring angrily at Grandma. Which is understandable, given that Grandma and Klaus Mettig had just been spotted in a heated embrace in the back of one of Anselm Kiefer's airplane installations.

Digital coloured photograph
NM
JG7912405

TOM WOLFE'S UMBRELLA (1986)

A blue umbrella that Wolfe, in ecstatic affection, threw after Grandma at a subway station at 85th Street and Lexington in New York. Grandma got off at the next station, took the train back in the opposite direction and hopped onto the tracks to retrieve the umbrella.

Polyester and oak
VG+ (good craftsmanship)
JG7912406

JENNY HOLZER'S RAMLÖSA BOTTLE (2002)

Grandma lived at Vanås castle in Sweden for two months while Holzer was installing the work "Vanås Wall" in the wooded area during the spring of 2002. Holzer almost went mad from all of the mosquitoes in the woods and constantly longed for her home in Hoosick Falls. Grandma massaged Holzer's temples each day with Ramlösa water, which she convinced Holzer had healing properties from a wellspring deep in Dalarna, thereby helping her to complete her work.

Plastic bottle with label
VG
JG7912407

MAX NEUHAUS' STAMP ON BAKING PAPER (1966)

Neuhaus stamped "Listen!" into the palm of all those who participated in his soundwalks in Manhattan. Planning accordingly, Grandma positioned a piece of baking paper in her palm when Neuhaus stamped it, which she then tucked away for safe keeping.

Baking paper
VG-
JG7912408

ALF PRØYSEN'S ROSE-PAINTED CHEST FROM SOUTH GUDBRANDSDALEN (1951)

Homemade, rose-painted wooden chest from the Fåberg region of Gudbrandsdal. Supposedly painted by Peter Friderichsen Kastrud. Gift to Grandma in 1951 as a thanks for her coaching during his work on the novel *Trost i taklampa*. On the base of the chest, Prøysen has written: "You are important. Alf."

Woodwork with metal fixtures and lock
G+ (key missing, but unlocked)
JG7912409

ERNST LUDWIG KIRCHNER'S BATHROBE (1906)

Zebra striped terry cloth bathrobe of German make by Richters. Given to Grandma after posing as a model in Warnemünde for Kirchner and Schmidt-Rottluff, on whom she made an indelible impression. Full of corks and receipts in the front pocket.

Coloured terry cloth
G- (awful smell, can possibly be cleaned)
JG7912410

LOUISE BOURGEOIS' SCULPTED LINEN BLANKET (1981)

200 x 80 cm linen blanket spotted with solidified residue and placenta. Shaped like an upside-down beehive, or oval cone, with a hole in the middle about the size of a newborn baby. Sculpted by Bourgeois during a road trip between Finnmark and Oslo in the winter of 1981.

Linen and human fluids
VG (some discolouration)
JG7912411

"NORDIC HERRING TRADITIONS", VOL. 2 (1979)

Book from Jotun Publisher about local traditions in Norway involving the production of pickled herring and hákarl, a type of cured Greenland shark. Purchased by Robert Maplethorpe and Patti Smith at Gyldendal Press's antique bookshop in Universitetsgata in 1979.

Hardbound book
VG-
JG7912412

PHOTOGRAPH OF HANS HAMMARSKJÖLD (1989)

Taken at Liseberg in Göteborg. Shows two young men who seem to be having a hilarious time posing as Conan and a Blues Brother.

Coloured photograph
VG+ (stamped Tiofoto on the back)
JG7912413

PICASSO'S BURST CONDOM (1941)

Remains of a burst white condom with an annoying strawberry smell. Originally employed during sexual intercourse with Pablo Picasso at a hotel in Nice. Grandma pressed her fingernail into the condom to make a small incision, hoping to become "involuntarily" pregnant with Picasso's child. She later bound both ends of the condom with fishing twine in order to store the sperm for future generations.

Rubber
G- (pulverized)
JG7912414

Dear Gustimoldo

All of the jutegnask has been removed from the house and the black signs brought in. It was as we feared—there is a cosmic equilibrium between jutegnask and the black signs. Besides reflecting on that idea, there is little else to do here. I sit in my small room and pass the days with intense sessions of sign hanging practice. It helps me to stay warm in the winter chill. I've set new records and tested advanced equipment for hanging the signs, but I have begun to realize that it no longer matters.

It is impossible to hang the black signs alone.

There is nonetheless one thing that helps me to get up in the morning—the postcards that you sent from your grand tour after your vanishing act. When I study the postcards, it strikes me that you went out on this global tour in order to check out whether all our theories about the world could hold any water. Did you hope to discover whether humankind really was gone, that we had been conquered? Was the trip your one last gesture to do the world a favour? The first days after you left, I was scared to death that you would discover goodness itself, or what's worse—that you would find that we could fit in—that there was a place for idiots like us. But after receiving a few postcards, I realized what it was about.

Poor you, Gustimoldo.

There are some futile moments as I browse through the stack of cards and think about what you have written there, when it feels as though you could appear at the door at any moment. You would stand there, suitcase in hand, and give me a strong hug. Ready for the task at hand.

All has been forgiven.

Gustimoldo—don't leave me here alone. Don't leave me unfinished. Don't let me become as disillusioned as the rest of them. Let us take this last stage, the round of victory, together.

Come home.
Come forth.

Dear Gustimoldo

Time passes much too slowly. Nothing works.

I pick up a postcard sent from Tijuana, Mexico. The front shows a green cactus wearing a sombrero. Inserted into the trunk of the cactus is a tap and flowing from the tap are precious drops of tequila. In the upper left corner, the words "Mexico Style" are written in a typeface that is supposed to mimic the prickly green cactus. On the back of the card, you have transcribed a portion of a poem that I have not been able to place.

> *Where should you go when the road runs in circles?*
> *Where should you go when you don't know your goal?*
> *Where should you hide when the stones cry?*
> *Where should you hide when the river boils?*
>
> *You yourself will become the run.*

There are six days and nine hours left until the last auction ends.

Dear Gustimoldo

I am reading a postcard that you sent me from the Giza pyramids in Egypt. Was it really you who wrote it? You start off by ranting about how the photograph must have either been photoshopped or else taken nine thousand years ago, since the present-day pyramids are not surrounded by a desert but rather rise out of a landfill scattered with camel droppings and electrical pylons strung at random in every which-way. You claim that the best place to view the Sphinx's nose is from a McDonald's, Pizza Hut, or KFC, since these companies have been allowed to erect an enormous restaurant complex directly at the Sphinx's haunches.

Before going to Giza, you had taken an excursion out in the Sahara desert on the border of Libya. On your way toward your camp, your group had met a band of desert nomads who wanted to show their woven rugs and offer apple tea. Since you were in the middle of a desert and weren't carrying any cash, you agreed a bit reluctantly to being given a display of local handicrafts and to enjoying tea in their tents. At the end, they of course asked whether you would like to purchase one of their rugs, and you answered by turning your pockets inside out. The nomads smiled smugly and pulled out a credit card pin pad that had satellite connection via mobile phone. In the middle of the desert. You ended up with a little knotted rug.

It was obvious that you didn't hit it off so well with the Sahara nomads. You ended your greeting by telling me about one night when you had to do your duty behind a sand dune in the pitch darkness of nightfall. The next morning, you woke before dawn to watch the world famous Sahara sunrise from atop the nearest sand dune. As the sun came up, gradually stretching out its light to reveal the desert, it also revealed that you had done your duty directly in front of a nomad family's tent. They stood down below, glaring angrily at you as they covered your excrement with sand. A small girl had been employed with removing your toilet paper from where it had wound itself around the tent line.

Only five days and 22 hours left.

Dear Gustimoldo

I am sitting in my crawl space, waiting. This morning I performed some interval training in sign hanging, but I was too unmotivated to improve my results. During the workout, I caught a glimpse of myself in the shiny surface of a black sign. There was a pale, thin little man in his underpants, a tool belt slung round his torso and small globs of yogurt solidified in his beard. The man was hanging signs as if his own life depended on it. The sight was disheartening. I was irritated at the slightest provocation for the rest of the day, and I lay down on my bed to read through the postcards.

"Reykjavik hot tub!" was written across the front of one. It was a photo of several people soaking in hot springs with white sulphur mud smeared across their faces. You had driven the island's circumference for a week, sleeping in the backseat of your rented car instead of checking into a hotel. A few days earlier, you had parked at a sandy beach on the outskirts of Hafnarfjordur to spend the night. You grilled Icelandic lamb on a disposable grill and slept with your car doors wide open while listening to the waves crashing onto land. The next morning, as you put on your trunks for a morning swim, you observed dozens of slippery, gleaming rocks on the beach that you hadn't noticed the night before. Believing that the tide had covered the rocks, you walked calmly down toward the beach with your hand towel clutched at your waist. But when you were only a few steps away, you suddenly stopped. The rocks were in fact a colony of seals sleeping peacefully on the beach. You walked between hundreds of the sleeping seals, an organic moonscape. After a few minutes of this paradise, you noticed a column of four-wheel drives on the horizon, heading in your direction. After two minutes, the beach was invaded by a group of Dutch seal spotters who hopped out of their jeeps to compete in getting the best snapshots. The seals woke up. You packed your things slowly into your car as you sobbed.

You end the card with these words:

> *The following night, I dreamt that I was a seal who dreamt.*

Dear Gustimoldo

Only four days and 22 hours until the auction is over. The postcard that I am holding in my hand was post stamped in Manaus deep in the Amazon. The front image is a photo of the town opera house, the Teatro Amazonas, which was the inspiration for Herzog's film *Fitzcarraldo*. That location must have been your goal for travelling here. Your journey took you by shuttle boat from the Amazon delta in Belem all the way up to the last stop in Manuas. Wide-eyed, you strung your hammock up right next to the belching diesel engine, and therefore did not get much sleep. The bunks next to you were occupied by a couple from England. In an acidic tone, you note that the English only travel to places where they can treat the natives as slaves. Isn't this nature in all of us, Gustimoldo? The thing that left the strongest impression on you during your trip up the Amazon is that the native people residing along the river followed after you in their rowboats. They used to come with painted faces, spears held high in defence of their territory. Now they were following to request that the tourists' trash be tossed overboard to them in plastic bags. You devote a bit of time to nature as well. You described the wide horizon of the Amazon that affixed itself to your memory. From your perch on the uppermost deck, you gazed out across the vast landscape and bore witness to numerous meteorological phenomena that you'd never before seen. Yesterday evening, you wrote, you could see four differing types of clouds floating silently in layers on the horizon. The top cloud rained onto the one beneath it, which received it and passed it on to the next one. And so on.

You concluded by recounting a conversation with a surgical nurse from Cologne. Over a glass of cachaça, she told you what kind of music the surgeons listen to during their operations. Not surprisingly, most of them like to put on classical music, especially Bach's cello suites with its steady rhythms that help the doctor maintain a good tempo during the procedure. One surgeon, who she often assisted, listened solely to the album *John Barry Plays the Great James Bond Themes* on full volume. An Indian surgeon listened to Jan Garbarek and Ustad Fateh Ali Kahn's *Ragas and Sagas*. She revealed to you that the best days at work were in the winter, when dead snowboarders and other avalanche victims were brought directly to the hospital. These generally young bodies were in near mint condition when they arrived, nothing was crushed, burned or gashed. On these night shifts, which were also well paid, she and her favourite surgeon fired up the rock band Nickelback's *Best-of* album on full blast and harvested a continuous stream of perfectly pristine organs throughout the night.

Dear Gustimoldo

The postcard in my hand has neither a postmark or stamp, but has nonetheless found its way into the mailbox. Have you been here?

In block letters, it says:

> When I hoped for good, evil came; and when I waited for light, then came darkness. I am churning within and cannot rest; days of suffering rise to meet me.

I know these words, Gustimoldo. They are from the Book of Job, and they are the lines that the priest uses in mass after suicide or tragic mishaps.

What do you want with me?

Dear Gustimoldo

You sent a postcard from Isla de la Juventud, Cuba. The photo on the front shows the island's prison, "Presidio Modelo", where Fidel Castro was incarcerated for two years after the unsuccessful coup of the Batista regime in 1953. You claim to have travelled there to study the effective architectural principles constituting the prison structure following Jeremy Bentham's Panopticon-style.

"Communism is nothing more than a poor-man's capitalism," is what Cuba has taught you. Everyone here is out to sell his sister because there's nothing else to sell. And every professor and laymen has a sister. And another thing. It isn't just in the American films that the whores say "fucky fucky" when you walk by. Maybe this isn't so surprising, since more than half of the tourists on the island are older Italian men on solo vacations? You befriended an American who calls himself Frank, an international whoremonger. Frank works in software some months of every year in Nevada and then travels for the rest of the year to Cuba, together with his cat Mingus, and chases girls. He goes about with a stack of Polaroid photos in his back pocket, snapshots of Cuban girls sitting half naked on the edge of a bed, posing before or after the deed. You write that he has employed two local Cuban "suppliers" to work full time for him, their sole task being to find girls, make an offer, haggle over the price and check the age on their ID cards. They earn good money. One evening when you returned late to the hotel, Frank was waiting for you in the bar. He suggested that he would treat you in accompanying him to a bordello. When you refused his invitation, he said something that will be difficult for you to forget: "You can't sit next to the pool all day long without dipping your toes in once." To lighten the mood, you asked whether he realized that, at the age of 56, he had bedded more ladies than Don Juan had managed in his lifetime, which was a mere 123. Frank's response was to enter into a spontaneous state of euphoria, ensconced in a colourful cloak of magnanimity. He had bested Don Juan, and proclaimed: "Love conquers all, so let's get on with it."

You end the postcard from Havana by writing about a policeman who patrols the area around your hotel in the Alamar district, who follows you each night as you make your way home. He trails a few paces behind you and hums Michael Jackson's "You Are Not Alone." This stripped-down, a cappella version of the song scares the shit out of you. You turn, offer him some pesos, and hurry to get away.

Three days and 12 hours left.

Dear Gustimoldo

I am staring at a postcard you sent from Florence. On the front is a photo of Michelangelo's four unfinished slave sculptures, which can be found in the Galleria d'Accademia—the slaves who fight to be released from the marble but never manage to escape its grip. On the back, you inform me that Michelangelo never got around to finishing the four sculptures because new popes required his time and talents for their own ornamentation instead of allowing him to complete old projects. The slaves were therefore imprisoned for all time in the stone. You report that you have just returned from Rome. Instead of visiting the Vatican and its museums, you locked yourself into your hotel room and watched the film "The Agony and the Ecstasy," in which Michelangelo is played by Charlton Heston. You now write that you are relaxing at a hotel in Florence and soon hope to find a restaurant with the most exquisite pasta al pomodoro in all of Tuscany. The only thing that could convince you to leave your hotel room would be if you would decide to go to Uffizi to see Leonardo da Vinci's "Adorazione dei Magi." You have been immersed in this painting for as long as I've known you. As a fifteen-year-old you hung a print of it on the best wall over your bed, where normal kids had Giggs or Metallica. The motif of the painting is often described as the moment of grace in which Jesus entered the world. Gustimoldo, I know that you have another opinion. In the brownish tempera hues, you see a horrific scene unfolding. The shepherds are in shock and the disciples are throwing themselves at Mary's feet in pure fear. There they lay, writhing in agony and it is only Mary and the child who do not realize what has occurred. You believe that da Vinci foresaw what the child Jesus would cause and how it would be exploited for all time to come.

In recent years, many art historians have presented evidence that Leonardo da Vinci was an atheist. It could be that your theory might actually be true this once.

Two days and four hours left.

Where are you, Gustimoldo?

Dear Gustimoldo

A postcard from Novi Beograd, Serbia. A photo of the Tito Museum.

On the back, you've written:

> *Give me the poor and forlorn*
> *those fearful and feeble men*
> *who restlessly swallow my narrow thought*
> *and die for it time and again*

A joke?

Dear Gustimoldo

I am looking at a postcard from Årjäng in Sweden. The front photo is a typical Swedish lake surrounded by pine trees stretching all the way down to the water. I know where you are. You have gone to find "the curve."

Three or four years ago, you clipped out a newspaper article about a traffic accident, where a boy from Årjäng had driven to his death. He entered the curve at a speed of over a hundred kilometres per hour and plunged straight into the forest. The article divulged that this was not the first time that the boy had lost control at the curve, but the ninth. Although he had been badly injured in almost every attempt, the boy couldn't let go of his goal to conquer the curve at 100 kph. The locals all thought this was pure stupidity, as it was clear to everyone that the turn in the road was so tight that even an experienced race car driver wouldn't be able to swing it. Added to that, the road just before the curve was downhill, which made it difficult for the wheels to grip. For several years, the village people had attempted to sway the boy from his idea to clear the curve. But the boy was stubborn. As soon as he was released from the hospital each time, he would begin repairing the damaged car in his father's barn. One girl who was interviewed tangentially to the newspaper article, revealed how she had once met the now-deceased boy at a party. He showed her his wallet, and in the plastic sleeve which usually contains photos of a girlfriend or family members, he had a photo of his skidding car. His eyes brimmed with tears.

As the matter became more well known in the local community, the sheriff had more trees cut down along the roadside to secure the curve. Urgent council meetings took place and it was decided that a crash barrier would be set up, even though outsiders considered this a gross waste of the local budget, since only three people lived so far out in the woods. But before the barrier could be erected, the boy went out on his ninth attempt. The Toyota veered off of the road and went into a roll. The boy shot right through the windshield. His body was only discovered the following morning, sunk down into the snow. The blood that had continuously pumped out of his body had served to melt the snow beneath him, creating a natural grave. The newspaper article ended with a shrewd detail. When the journalist from the local newspaper came to his father's door, the first thing he said was: "He's gone and done it now, hasn't he?"

Dear Gustimoldo

I have stopped my sign-hanging exercises. I now pass entire days laying on the bed, breathing and writing you letters. I am as desolate as a person can be—left alone with millions of black signs and a villa in ruins. On my pillow is one of the last postcards that you sent before it all stopped. The postmark shows that you sent it off from a mailbox near Chengdu, China. On the front, a picture of two panda bears at a reserve. They look so lazy and apathetic that one could easily mistake them for people in panda costumes who can't be bothered to play their roles credibly.

You write that you are sitting alone at a restaurant that serves food from the Hunan district. Everyone around you is sharing their meal with a family, friends or lover. You can see the humour in the situation, that in the most populated country in the world, which has over half a billion girls, you are sitting there so solitarily alone and cannot find a single person to share a meal with.

Later, you've written a single sentence in another ink colour:

> *The sound you heard was a glacier collapsing in the night*

Meaning?

Dear Gustimoldo

There is less than a day left before the auction ends. Only 19 hours now. In my trembling hand, I am holding several of the empty postcards that you sent from Nairobi, Melbourne, Cork, St. Petersburg, and Longyearbyen. Did you mean to indicate that you were still alive but without anything further to report?

You decided to mail them, nonetheless.

Dear Gustimoldo

There's one postcard from Wannsee where you've written three separate sentences that I can't get out of my head. It's as if they are embossed on the card's surface.

They sit with winds on a leash, pulling them across the meadows

Our darkness divides us

Remain true to that which is unstable in life

Are the sentences related in any way?

Dear Gustimoldo

Tonight saw the first snowfall and there's frost licking at the windowpanes. There's probably good skiing to be had in Nordmarka now. I'm sitting in my hovel, frostbitten and looking at the last postcards you sent me from Argentina. They are glued and taped together, forming a small book that must be cut open with some force. I haven't yet dared to open this last sign of life from you for fear of what it might contain. The top card shows Teatro Colón in all its glory. On another, one can see Carlos Gardel drinking *mate* at a sidewalk cafe in San Telmo. From what I can decipher of the handwriting on the back, you write that a feeling of peace has come over you in Argentina, a sense that breathing is no longer so difficult, as though being on the opposite side of the globe, away from the signs, brings relief. I rip several of the cards from the stack. One is covered by brown packing tape, but I can still see the outline of Patagonia's treeless landscape underneath. You write that you are planning to take the bus to Santiago de Chile and then to secure plane tickets to the Easter Islands with the singular goal of bedding a grass-skirted native. Many blank postcards follow this one. Then a card with a picture of a gaucho, riding across a pampas in full gallop, where you have written three sentences on the address lines:

The Bible was never fully written.
Your part was written.
Call and say thanks in a few years.

An apology?

I pull the postcards apart, one after another. It is almost impossible to move my fingers, they are covered in glue and tape. Several more blank postcards without any communication from you. One was sent from the northern city Salta, and shows a salt desert on the front. Another portrays the beautiful borderlands between Argentina, Bolivia and Paraguay with a chain of pink and turquoise mountains. There's one with Maradona outside of Boca Junior's stadium. One with a panoramic photo of Avenida Nuevo de Julio which says "Buenos Aires by Night" across the front of the photo. One with the inflatable Jesus statue in Tierra Santa. One with the writing desk of Borges. One with roasted Tierra del Fuego lamb. One with seagulls from Ushuaia. The last postcard shows a hunter from one of the Amazon's native tribes, his body submerged under water. The postcard stands out and doesn't have anything to do with Argentina, does it, Gustimoldo? The hunter has pulled the hollowed-out carcass of a small pelican over his head so that he can swim with his body beneath the water, sneak up on birds, and act like he is one of them. On the backside, you've written in blue pen:

> He who puts the Devil on his shoulders must bear
> him forward.

I walk out onto the veranda, hold my hands up toward the sky and accept everything that falls into them.

Down fall millions of black signs.